618·76 MAR.

7190

ED
D

COPING WITH POSTNATAL DEPRESSION

FIONA MARSHALL has wide experience as a jour-
nalist and author. She is also the author of *Coping
Successfully with your Second Child* (Sheldon 1992) and
Losing a Parent (Sheldon Insight 1993). She lives with
her family in south-west London.

Overcoming Common Problems Series

For a full list of titles please contact
Sheldon Press, Marylebone Road, London NW1 4DU

Beating the Blues
SUSAN TANNER AND JILLIAN
BALL

Birth Over Thirty
SHEILA KITZINGER

Body Language
How to read others' thoughts by their
gestures
ALLAN PEASE

Calm Down
How to cope with frustration and anger
DR PAUL HAUCK

Changing Course
How to take charge of your career
SUE DYSON AND STEPHEN HOARE

Comfort for Depression
JANET HORWOOD

Complete Public Speaker
GYLES BRANDRETH

Coping Successfully with Migraine
SUE DYSON

**Coping Successfully with Your Child's
Asthma**
DR PAUL CARSON

**Coping Successfully with Your Hyperactive
Child**
DR PAUL CARSON

**Coping Successfully with Your Irritable
Bowel**
ROSEMARY NICOL

**Coping Successfully with Your Second
Child**
FIONA MARSHALL

Coping with Anxiety and Depression
SHIRLEY TRICKETT

Coping with Blushing
DR ROBERT EDELMANN

Coping with Cot Death
SARAH MURPHY

Coping with Depression and Elation
DR PATRICK McKEON

Coping with Stress
DR GEORGIA WITKIN-LANOIL

Coping with Strokes
DR TOM SMITH

Coping with Suicide
DR DONALD SCOTT

Coping with Thrush
CAROLINE CLAYTON

Curing Arthritis – The Drug-Free Way
MARGARET HILLS

Curing Arthritis Diet Book
MARGARET HILLS

**Curing Coughs, Colds and Flu – The
Drug-Free Way**
MARGARET HILLS

Curing Illness – The Drug-Free Way
MARGARET HILLS

Depression
DR PAUL HAUCK

Divorce and Separation
ANGELA WILLANS

Don't Blame Me!
How to stop blaming yourself
and other people
TONY GOUGH

**Everything You Need to Know about
Adoption**
MAGGIE JONES

**Everything You Need to Know about
Osteoporosis**
ROSEMARY NICOL

**Everything You Need to Know about
Shingles**
DR ROBERT YOUNGSON

**Family First Aid and Emergency
Handbook**
DR ANDREW STANWAY

Feverfew
DR STEWART JOHNSON

Overcoming Common Problems Series

Fight Your Phobia and Win
DAVID LEWIS

Getting Along with People
DIANNE DOUBTFIRE

Getting Married
JOANNA MOORHEAD

Goodbye Backache
DR DAVID IMRIE WITH COLLEEN
DIMSON

Heart Attacks – Prevent and Survive
DR TOM SMITH

Helping Children Cope with Divorce
ROSEMARY WELLS

Helping Children Cope with Grief
ROSEMARY WELLS

Helping Children Cope with Stress
URSULA MARKHAM

Hold Your Head Up High
DR PAUL HAUCK

How to be a Successful Secretary
SUE DYSON AND STEPHEN HOARE

How to Be Your Own Best Friend
DR PAUL HAUCK

How to Control your Drinking
DRS W. MILLER AND R. MUNOZ

How to Cope with Splitting Up
VERA PEIFFER

How to Cope with Stress
DR PETER TYRER

How to Cope with Tinnitus and Hearing
Loss
DR ROBERT YOUNGSON

How to Cope with Your Child's Allergies
DR PAUL CARSON

How to Do What You Want to Do
DR PAUL HAUCK

How to Get Things Done
ALISON HARDINGHAM

How to Improve Your Confidence
DR KENNETH HAMBLY

How to Interview and Be Interviewed
MICHELE BROWN AND GYLES
BRANDRETH

How to Love a Difficult Man
NANCY GOOD

How to Love and be Loved
DR PAUL HAUCK

How to Make Successful Decisions
ALISON HARDINGHAM

How to Move House Successfully
ANNE CHARLISH

How to Negotiate Successfully
PATRICK FORSYTH

How to Pass Your Driving Test
DONALD RIDLAND

How to Solve Your Problems
BRENDA ROGERS

How to Spot Your Child's Potential
CECILE DROUIN AND ALAIN DUBOS

How to Stand up for Yourself
DR PAUL HAUCK

How to Start a Conversation and Make
Friends
DON GABOR

How to Stop Smoking
GEORGE TARGET

How to Stop Taking Tranquillisers
DR PETER TYRER

How to Stop Worrying
DR FRANK TALLIS

How to Study Successfully
MICHELE BROWN

How to Survive Your Teenagers
SHELIA DAINOW

How to Untangle Your Emotional Knots
DR WINDY DRYDEN AND JACK
GORDON

Hysterectomy
SUZIE HAYMAN

The Incredible Sulk
DR WINDY DRYDEN

Overcoming Common Problems Series

Overcoming Common Problems

COPING WITH
POSTNATAL DEPRESSION

Fiona Marshall

First published in Great Britain in 1993
Sheldon Press, SPCK, Marylebone Road, London NW1 4DU

© Fiona Marshall 1993

British Library Cataloguing-in-Publication Data
A catalogue record for this book is available from the British Library
ISBN 0–85969–681–2

Photoset by Deltatype Ltd, Ellesmere Port, Cheshire
Printed in Great Britain by Biddles Ltd, Guildford and King's Lynn

Contents

Acknowledgements

My grateful thanks to all the women who shared their experience with me and so made possible the writing of this book. Special thanks to the Association of Postnatal Illness, in particular Clare Delpech, Secretary of the Association, Sarah Gutch, Jean Gellatly; Dr Trevor Friedman, consultant liaison psychiatrist at Leicester General Hospital and Secretary of the Marcé Society.

Introduction

First things first – postnatal depression does pass. It's important to state this at the very beginning, because if ever a woman needed to lay hold of hope, it's when she's in the throes of this bleak and apparently endless condition. While there is still some confusion about the causes and nature of postnatal depression, two things are clear: women do recover from it, and it is treatable, in a number of ways. Professionals such as counsellors are understandably cautious about handing out guarantees of absolute recovery, but there are many women only too happy to tell you how they managed to put their depression behind them.

Some of their stories you will meet in this book, and it is hoped that by reading case histories which have a positive outcome, you will be encouraged to believe that your own depression will lift one day. This isn't to gloss over suffering with easy reassurances which only serve to increase despair. Postnatal depression causes too much distress to be taken other than seriously. However, a longer-term view is needed than perhaps you may be willing to allow when plunged into the depths of depression. This book aims to provide that view, to look beyond the present at a time when the future may only mean wondering how on earth to summon the will to change the baby's nappy again. And if your depression has passed or is passing, it is hoped that this book will help you to a deeper understanding of what happened to you. It's also possible that you're reading this because someone close to you is suffering from postnatal depression, in which case you will find specific advice on how to help as well as general information about the condition. Fathers especially are sometimes overlooked when it comes to this kind of depression; the book describes how they can be affected both directly and indirectly, and suggests action they can take too.

This book defines depression quite widely, looking at as many contributing factors as possible – physical, psychological and social. In this way, it aims to give plenty of scope for women to identify with the feelings described, important because part of postnatal depression is that women don't always realize they are suffering from it. This is partly because it is naturally hard to admit that there is anything wrong, especially after a birth when everyone expects you to be unremittingly delighted with your new baby. It is also because depression itself can be understood as an emotion, or as a condition. When we think of depression, we do tend to think of being 'depressed' or down, and to look for feelings which match. But postnatal depression doesn't necessarily make you feel like this, although being the protean condition it is, it may do.

So, how can you expect to feel if you do have postnatal depression? Maybe you're simply dead tired – too exhausted to clean the kitchen, to put the baby's dirty clothes on to wash. All you feel capable of is sitting down with a coffee and thinking about how awful you feel. The baby wakes at night and won't go back to sleep, crying endlessly until you cry too, with sheer tiredness and with not knowing how you're ever going to manage with the inescapable responsibility of this tiny human being. These feelings of exhaustion and being unable to cope are two of the most common symptoms associated with postnatal depression. This at once raises the question of how far postnatal depression differs from the experience of most mothers with a new baby; but of this, more later in the book! The same question is raised by another symptom – deep feelings of isolation, of the rest of the world having gone away.

Other signs of depression, described more fully in chapter 1, are many, although it is unlikely that you will have them all. Women often speak of a particular aspect which has made life so difficult. For one, it may be the torment of not being able to sleep no matter how tired she is; for another, a deep need for sleep which is never satisfied; for yet another, sleep interrupted by appalling nightmares. Feelings of unworthiness, anxiety, panic, eating disorders, tension, confused or obsessional thinking, lack of concentration or forgetfulness, loss of interest in sex – these are just some of the main signs that you may be suffering from depression caused by having a baby.

Speaking of which! Part of the great distress this condition causes can be inappropriate thoughts towards the baby, a fear of harming her, or a constant, draining anxiety about her well-being. Some find it deeply distressing that they can't relate to their child better, perhaps don't have the expected feelings of love. But many women have spoken of how the baby was the one bright spot in their lives, how the baby made it all bearable, how the baby kept them going.

Nonetheless, love does allow room for the emotions of depression, notably ambivalence. In other words, you can still love your baby even if you do experience darker emotions and doubts about motherhood; and, just because you've had a baby, it shouldn't mean you stop caring about yourself. So, what about you? After all, pregnancy is a time when you, the future mother, are 'babied' – the centre of attention, urged to rest, asked how you're feeling. Yet, after the birth, just when you'e exhausted and aching and really need some attention, the new baby gets it all! But this displacement of yourself by the baby goes much deeper than this. Having a baby means a fundamental letting go of yourself: it means saying goodbye to your own childhood and a whole set of attitudes which went with being a child. The grief aspect of postnatal depression needs attention, with all its underlying feelings of loss and resentment – the very feelings a mother is not supposed to have.

For many years indeed, and not so long ago, postnatal depression was something you didn't talk about. Nowadays, while it is realized that this is by far the worst way to deal with it, mothers are still prey to social and biological demands that the baby comes first, while their own needs are denied – a conflict which classically finds an outlet in depression. On a practical level, this can still mean not asking for any treatment, and so delaying recovery, sometimes until breaking point is reached. Part of coming to terms with motherhood is acknowledging these more negative feelings – the anger, the enduring instinct of 'me first' – even if this means going against conventional views of parenthood. It should also mean feeling that you have the right to treatment without judgement and, ideally, getting that treatment sooner rather than later. Why suffer for longer than you have to when help is available?

Postnatal depression still arouses a great variety of responses, from the serious medical belief that the causes and cure are hormonal (and treatable), to the little thought-out injunction to 'Pull yourself together – it's all in the mind'. My own view of the subject has been as catholic as possible. As a mother of two children, I have been left with the impression that there is something in the nature of postnatal depression which touches all women. While researching this book, I have been struck again and again by the immediate interest – often the passion – shown by women the minute the subject was mentioned, the way each one assumed that it has meaning for her, whether she had suffered from depression or not. It seems to be a long-term meaning too: another interesting point was how older women interviewed could still bring out sharp memories of their own depression while watching their grand-children play.

While this book was in progress, I interviewed a number of women across a broad spectrum of ages and backgrounds in order to give as full a view as possible of postnatal depression. While your own experience will always be unique, it is hoped that this approach will give a representative view of postnatal depression which at the same time leaves room for the variety which is such a hallmark of this condition. Whether you had a baby when you were younger or older, whether your main symptom was exhaustion or rage, whether you had family support or not – in many ways, postnatal depression is no respector of circumstances. Talking of support from the family, many women have spoken warmly of the help they received from their partners. Maybe this hasn't been your experience – perhaps you are a single mother, or perhaps you are unfortunate enough to have a partner who was 'emotionally unavailable' just when you needed him in your depression. Not all women have partners; not all women have good, supportive partners. But this doesn't mean they can't recover from postnatal depression – indeed, coming out of the depression into new emotional independence is a theme which may have even deeper resonances for them.

The concensus of such women seems to be that conventional expectations don't allow a place for the profound adjustment, physical and emotional, that has to take place after a birth; in some, it is just all too much, and depression appears. Having a baby is such a huge life change, and involves such a massive shift in identity, that it is impossible to avoid some similar massive shift in your own emotions. It is hardly too fanciful to say that the mother is re-born with the baby: his birth is one of your initiations into life. Regarded in this light, depression can be a path into a new way of being, even if it may not feel like it at the time.

Then there's the quality of care needed – demanded – by all tiny children. You can never switch off from this level of care, which absorbs much of your creative energy so that you may have to give up activities which are important to you. The result is a lowering of vitality which, at the time, feels as if it will never pass; again, the frustration and anger this involves can play a part in depression. Perhaps it serves a useful purpose in slowing your pace to that of a small child; certainly, many parents have spoken of how they discovered a new lease of life once their child was a little older. The last chapter of this book explores the possible usefulness of depression, the different messages it could be giving you: to slow down, to rest, to change.

In general, this book tends to focus more on this kind of unobtrusive, lingering dissatisfaction, rather than the more dramatic psychotic end of postnatal illness (although it is very important to acknowledge just how serious it can be). It is concerned with the mother who doesn't really know what is wrong but who feels that life has somehow lost its colour; the one who feels she can't talk to any of her friends about the way she feels in case they echo her fear that she's going mad; the one who increasingly feels trapped in a world of her own with fewer and fewer outside contacts; in other words, anyone suffering from that quiet, creeping despair whose cumulative effect, over the weeks and months, can be so sad and destructive.

Sad is the word. Contrary to popular expectations, it *can* be sad work having a baby, but it's the kind of sadness that goes with having your life torn out by its roots. Pregnancy, birth and childcare involve tremendous physical and emotional upheaval, and it is this that the antenatal classes so often don't prepare you for. Could they anyway? Because just as no one can have the baby for you, no one can anticipate your feelings for you, or live through them for you. In the same way, no one can say exactly when you will feel better. But the likelihood is that you *will* feel better. It may take time and care, perhaps a struggle with aspects of yourself which you could never have foreseen during pregnancy. You may have to seek outside help when you would much rather have managed alone. But whatever happens, don't be hard on yourself. Motherhood brings many complex emotions at the best of times, and depression can be a very difficult route through these. This book is a recognition of the fact that no woman should have to walk that route alone; plenty of other people have been this way too – enough to point the way to the renewed self-esteem and happiness which can be waiting at the other end.

1
What is Postnatal Depression?

Nothing should really be wrong. You've recently had a baby, surely the crowning fulfilment in a woman's life. Your baby is probably healthy, perfect and the result of a carefully planned pregnancy or at least a happy accident. In a civilized country, you have a roof over your head, access to water, food and medical supplies, and probably more – an adequate home, comfort, friends. Of course you have problems – not enough money, a partner who's unhappy with his work – but don't we all? Why then can't you begin to be reasonably happy? Why do you feel that life is full of darkness? Where has that constant ache of fear come from, the feeling that you've suddenly lost the skin which protected you from the horrors of life? You've lost the skin that enabled you to take things in your stride, and are now reduced to someone who's left quivering with irritability at the least demand from your partner or the baby, someone who feels constantly under attack, someone who's divided from tears only by the thinnest barrier, someone who feels absolutely blank with misery.

Not all of these feelings may apply to you. The above is a composite picture of how postnatal depression can affect you, put together from interviews with several women who contributed to the making of this book. But, the more subtle effects can be destructive too: a haunting lack of structure, the growing guilt, the uneasy feeling that your control of life is gradually slipping away from you, that your choices are slowly diminishing and will never revive again. There is also one of depression's cruellest illusions, the feeling that now you know the final truth about life, now all the pretence has been stripped away, leaving the bare rock of horror beneath. This is what it always has been like, this is the deepest reality; and all happiness, all self-forgetful activity, is just foliage which blooms briefly and then fades uselessly away.

In fact, it is often the depression which fades away. Uselessly? Not altogether. Many women do eventually find that the experience can become a source of strength and maturity, even if they lost all emotional balance while going through it. More important to realize now, with time and perhaps with treatment, is that happiness does return, that innocent enjoyment of life which relishes a brisk walk or a trip to the shops, which can take pleasure in a changing season or in planning a dinner menu, above all, which can forget, relax, sleep. In other words, normality returns, and the mundane has a special charm for those who have been through emotional pain. With this in mind, before reading further, try thinking of three or four things which make the world seem the right way up to you, no matter how trivial, banal or clinchéd. A cup of tea? Neatly-tidied drawers? The smell of toast or coffee? A trip to the seaside? A spring day? An old toy from childhood? An old memory? In a world where the ground is constantly being cut from beneath your feet by depression, the most everyday likings can be valuable evidence of enduring solidity. Whatever your present pain, the cry of 'I just want to feel normal again', all too common in postnatal depression, is a wish that *can* be fulfilled.

Defining postnatal depression

There seem to be almost as many versions of postnatal depression as there are women, and about as many theories as to what causes it. It is hormonal, it is due to unresolved childhood traumas, it is the stress of parenthood in modern society, it is because childbirth isn't properly recognized as a rite of passage – take your pick. Indeed, postnatal depression is one of those subjects on which everyone seems to have an opinion. Like breastfeeding, it is a topic which takes a strong hold on the emotions and imaginations even of those not directly concerned. However, its emotive nature doesn't always make postnatal depression easily understood, particularly as to where it fits in between different disciplines such as obstetrics, psychiatry and sociology.

Before looking at external interpretations of depression, what about internal ones? What about the women who have actually been through the depression: how do they sum it up? While working on this book, I interviewed many women whose different experiences form an integral part of this book. Lucy, an adult education lecturer who had her first baby at 33, looks back at a depression which took place two years previously.

'I barely knew postnatal depression existed until I found myself going through it. For me, and I'm sure for others, it was an extremely complex experience, something which absorbed the whole of me – physically, emotionally, even spiritually if you like. I suppose the good thing about it was that the depression led me to look at things in myself which I was frightened of, the past, my father's death, aspects of myself. I had counselling, terrified of what was going to come out. The truth was never as bad as my fears. Now, I feel I've cleared so much up. I don't regret having gone through it, I'm even grateful, because I've discovered a whole section of life which I didn't know existed, just as I wasn't aware of depression and what people go through with it. It's as if I can now see a part of life which was always invisible before and I definitely feel stronger for that.'

In something of the same spirit, Tara, a 27-year-old boutique manager, speaks of the results of her depression.

'It was an awful time, really grey. My clearest memory is of one day standing watching some tennis with my husband and feeling absolutely dead inside, no feelings at all. I couldn't even cry. That was the real rock bottom, and that tends to be my reference point today – if I feel bad, I know it's never as bad as that awful day. In fact I don't think anything *will* ever be as bad, because I've left that part of my life behind now, that part of myself. Actually I think I was very immature; my priorities are completely different today.'

While 'growth through pain' cliches may add insult to injury when you're really down, it has to be said that many women speaking of a depression now behind them have described how much they learned from it. It may be helpful to bear this in mind when considering exactly what postnatal depression is, because if nothing else it is experience – an experience where the subjective approach is often stronger than objective research in terms of giving meaning. In other words, what's happened to you is, in the end, best explained by what makes sense to you. For example, it's no good an outsider, however kindly, saying, 'Your depression is a result of the low social status of mothers in the West', if you feel it's because you haven't had an unbroken night since some remote time back in pregnancy, or that your own family tensions, perhaps aggravated by the depression, need more urgent sorting out than your social status. It is always important to remember that your experience of depression is different to other people's. So, when reading, it is a good idea to look for what you do identify with, for what is helpful, and simply to leave what isn't.

One point where this is particularly relevant – postnatal illness can sometimes be extremely serious. As you can see from the description in the next chapter, puerperal psychosis, the extreme end of postnatal illness, is a rare but frightening condition in which a woman can lose touch with reality and be a danger to herself and to her baby. Depression itself can also sometimes bring some women extremely low, so that their perception of reality becomes distorted, even to the extent that they consider suicide. Until comparatively recently, not much attention was paid to postnatal illness by the medical profession, and there was a corresponding ignorance among mothers; because of this, some literature tends to emphasize the graver, if rarer, aspects, in the hope of saving those mothers who might injure themselves or their babies if left without help. Some women have been thoroughly frightened by reading about the more dramatic cases, even though these are relatively uncommon. So, when reading (or hearing) about someone whose situation seems worse than yours, there is no need to try and identify with it, or to fear that 'this too will happen to me'. Postnatal depression can, sadly, make women feel at the absolute end of their tether, even insane; on the other hand, you're not disqualified from depression if your own feelings happen to be milder. Your own level of distress is what counts.

If you *are* frightened about your condition, or about the safety of your baby or yourself, it is vital to get help without delay. You must talk to someone, be it your doctor, health visitor, mother or friend. There are also organizations specifically for the depressed or lonely which will respect confidentiality if you feel you have no one you can trust and want to get in touch anonymously; contact numbers are at the end of this book under Useful Addresses. And remember, you don't have to wait until you become desperate before you seek help.

Symptoms of postnatal depression

So, how can you tell if you *do* have postnatal depression? A pertinent question because it seems that there is something in the nature of this depression which makes the sufferers themselves miss it sometimes, although in fact some psychiatrists say that *all* depression is under-recognized and under-treated. Perhaps it's that you don't expect your depression to express itself as bad temper or lack of appetite; perhaps you're too preoccupied with caring for and worrying about the baby; perhaps it's simply because you don't expect it to happen to you. And the fact that depression takes so many forms can be confusing.

What's also confusing is that other postnatal disorders can be called postnatal depression even though they are not really the same. For example, the 'baby blues' reduce many women to tears soon after the birth, but aren't generally regarded as that serious. At the other extreme, puerperal psychosis can be extremely serious, if much rarer. Neither of these is what's meant by postnatal depression, and they are considered as separate disorders which are described in more detail further on.

Yet again, postnatal depression itself is sometimes subdivided into depression and exhaustion – but where does the exhaustion end and the depression begin? Perhaps it's more helpful to think in terms of degree: are your feelings mild or severe? All mothers feel extremely tired at times, all have their low moments: it's when these moods spread and spread into daily life, when they take over, that you need to be alert. In one sense, it doesn't matter *what* you call it. It's more important to be aware of what you're feeling, and to ask yourself some basic questions: Are you feeling down or even ill? How long has this been going on for? Are you disappointed in motherhood? Do you feel you can't cope? – and so on.

The depression can develop slowly from the baby blues, or start a few weeks or months after the birth. How long does it last? This varies greatly: some women find the worst is over by three or six months, while anecdotal evidence from some postnatal counsellors suggests that some women recover when the baby is around nine months old. Many parents have a tough first year, depressed or not. Some depressed mothers speak of a difficult first eighteen months, while a few, who may well have underlying long-term problems, talk in terms of years. The important point to remember is that outside help can always cut the time of suffering short.

'I never used to . . .'

This can be a general alert sign: 'I never used to cry so easily/wake up early/yell at my husband so often.' This sort of comment can be an indication that all is not well. You do need to differentiate between the normal life changes a baby brings and a growing, abnormal depression. 'I never used to skimp the washing-up/find cooking such a bore/leave beds unmade' are all quite normal comments in a life dominated by a baby! It is when it applies to a growing loss of emotional control in you, or an increasing inability to cope, that it's worth taking note. If you find yourself thinking, 'I never used to . . .' with a great deal of distress, it could be because of a vague realization that you are not feeling that well, over and above the fact that life is being made more difficult by the demands of a baby.

Postnatal exhaustion

'Oh, and the fatigue! I had two children with a short gap in between – I think I was tired for five years. I'm convinced that simple tiredness played a major part in my depression.'

Suzanne, 39, a playgroup leader who had two children at 30 and 32, suffered badly from postnatal depression: seven years after her depression she could still recall that crushing fatigue clearly. Closely linked with postnatal depression, postnatal exhaustion could probably be cured by what so many new mothers long for in vain – sleep, and lots of it. It has certainly been said that more rest in the early months and weeks of motherhood might well prevent much depression. Depressed mothers

11

report feeling utterly drained, as if the lifeblood had been sucked out of them; so do mothers who don't consider themselves depressed. What is said to distinguish the two is that if you're not depressed a few good nights will put you right; if you are depressed, they won't. Some also say that no matter how much sleep a depressed woman has, it is never enough and she always wants more. But exhaustion is more than a matter of collapsing into bed. It is a mental exhaustion too, a general lack of energy and interest which can dramatically curtail your life. Everything seems too much effort and life itself loses most of its interest; many women find this extreme tiredness and lethargy one of the most distressing symptoms.

Sleeping difficulties

Other kinds of problems with sleep can also form a part of depression: the inability to go to sleep at all, trouble going back to sleep once woken, early morning waking. Nightmares have also been reported. Marcia, 26, had trouble sleeping for the first fifteen months of her son's life.

'That symptom alone was what made me go for help, and the doctor at once said it was postnatal depression. I just couldn't sleep – it was so annoying as my son slept through the night from three months, which shows it wasn't because of a baby disrupting my sleep. I think myself it was just anxiety. The first child – no experience with babies – the responsibility.'

Early morning waking in particular is a classic sign of depression; though if your baby is also an early riser, or indeed a chronic night-waker, it can be hard to tell whether you're depressed anyway, or depressed because you're short of sleep.

Irritability

A natural consequence of lack of sleep, irritability has also been put down to hormonal factors, and so is seen by some as a highly important symptom. Irritation may be expressed in words or in actions, sometimes even in violence.

Lucy described how she constantly 'took it out' on her mother and husband in the months of her depression; Tara would break cups and destroy her favourite objects, such as a fine lace blouse that had belonged to her grandmother, and a vase given her by her partner for a birthday, crying bitterly afterwards. Naturally, relations suffered with their bewildered partners.

Some of the self-destructive nature of postnatal depression can be seen in the fact that Tara destroyed her favourite objects. These uncontrollable outbursts of anger are frightening for the woman concerned as well as for her partner, and even more frightening if you happen to feel angry with the baby, although it must be stressed that by no means everyone feels negative towards the baby. Some women report this kind of irritability particularly with older children after the birth of a new baby.

Tension and panic

Feeling on edge, being unable to relax, the feeling that you are under stress – all these use up energy and leave you with a low flash point, and such feelings may well lie behind irritability. It may be that the birth has left you 'wound up', or the nonstop nature of babycare has made you feel that you *can't* have a moment off to relax. Whichever way, depression can be expressed as tension. Panic attacks can be another unpleasant symptom.

Not coping

A growing inability to cope is a classic sign of postnatal depression. Sometimes not coping can extend to babycare, with the baby going short of feeds and nappy changes because the mother isn't fully aware of the baby's needs. But it's important to distinguish between real neglect of the baby and just the feeling that you can't keep to the ideal routine. No baby keeps to the ideal routine, but if you are depressed you may be much more sensitive to your baby's supposed irregularities. Every mother gets swamped by babycare and all her other tasks, but if you are depressed it tends to be far less easy to stay on top of the basics. Perhaps the difference is best illustrated by two quotes, the first from Bea, the mother of a one-year-old and a three-year-old who did not suffer from depression.

'I think my two must get a peculiar idea of housework because all they ever see me do is put the toilet brush down the loo every day! I do keep on top of the washing up. I shop once a week, on Thursdays when it's late night opening, because my husband can look after the children then. The washing machine gets used every day. I let the house go during the day – it's a MESS – but I do insist on a tidy-up time every evening!'

And so on. Bea, even if the house is untidy, has some points which she sticks to, some sort of system to get her through the week. The exhausting, muddled nature of depression is described by Lucy:

'The baby's room is a shambles but you lack the system others seem to have – you just don't know where to put things. What should go in which drawer? It all seems so confusing – and this from someone who used to prepare a lecture from a dozen sources with no problem! You can't bring yourself to empty the nappy bucket, not through laziness, but because the dustbin outside is full and you can't quite work out where you should put those used nappies. Dirty and clean clothes are just thrown into corners and left. There would be days when there literally wasn't an inch of uncovered floor space in the baby's room and I'd step carefully over it all, thinking, "I'll tidy it all up soon". Soon never came. Your mind comes up with objections to every task, and you find yourself going obsessively over your own condition. How can you get through this and what's it all about anyway? It uses up so much of you, there's little energy left for what's outside.'

Lucy's quote shows that although the mother may seem to be doing nothing, her thoughts are hard work enough. Not coping with the outside world often means a desperate inner struggle to cope with the depression.

Confused or obsessive thinking

Lucy's words go some way towards showing how easily confused thinking can be part of postnatal depression. Another symptom is obsessive thinking. This can be something particular, such as the fear that your husband may be having an affair. Or it can be a more wayward kind of obsession, which latches on to whatever subject you happen to think of. A typical worry could be some aspect of babycare, such as how much milk to give the baby, or perhaps an environmental concern – a fear about the world into which you have brought a child, such as the number of cars in the UK or the worsening pollution of the atmosphere (fears which may be as much about motherhood as about outside issues).

Depression can manifest itself as other disruptions to thinking, such as lack of concentration for activities like reading books or watching television. Linked to this is forgetfulness, a symptom of postnatal depression shared to some degree by other mothers, possibly because of hormonal changes, possibly because of lack of sleep or the pressure of the new job of babycare. In depression, this kind of forgetfulness may need more attention if it extends to care of the baby, with the mother forgetting when she gave the last feed or nappy change, or forgetting to give the next one.

Feelings of isolation

One of the worst aspects of the depression is the isolation that so many mothers feel, the conviction that there is no one else there, no one to talk to, no one who would understand. You may feel that other mothers are coping whereas you're not, and so you can't bear to see them, or you may simply feel too crushed by the depression. In some, this extends to not answering the doorbell or phone, a fairly severe symptom of depression.

Feelings of sadness and morbidity

While depression takes so many forms, simply feeling depressed and sad are obvious signs which are sometimes overlooked. There are days when little things are enough to set the tears going; others where a mood of despondency lies so heavy that crying would be a relief. Bursting into tears for no real reason is a symptom reported by many. Indeed, it has been said that one of the easiest ways to diagnose postnatal depression is to ask the woman how she's feeling and wait for her to burst into tears. One aspect of this general 'down' feeling is entering too readily into the sorrows of others – a kind of morbidity – as described by Tara:

'One friend of mine had a stillbirth. I felt almost as if it had been me – that I'd lost my baby. It was as if my mind would just grab whatever sad news there was around, and hang on to it – stories in the newspaper. If the people were the same age as me, or had children – any link in common – I'd feel as if I knew them, and I'd mourn personally for whatever bad thing had happened to them.'

With this heightened sensitivity, many mothers have had Tara's experience of not wanting to read the papers, or watch the news on television. In fact this stance, though modified, continues to form part of many parents' make-up: few people regard the news in the same way once they have a child. Often, however, you may feel sad for no reason, perhaps why other people's news makes a good hook to hang it on.

Guilt and unworthiness

Both of these emotions can be closely allied to morbidity. You may feel simply that you don't deserve to be a mother or that you're not equipped to care properly for a baby. This may be because of ignorance about babies, whose habits are often far more irregular than expected; it's easy to blame yourself when you don't 'get it right' with regard to routine. You may feel generally guilty and ungrateful that you're not happier with a nice enough home, a good enough partner, and a perfect little baby. Guilt can also be related to a specific cause, perhaps that you didn't 'do better' in some way at the birth, or that you 'failed' at breastfeeding, even that you didn't produce the sex of child that your partner wanted – the list is endless.

15

To some extent, guilt comes with motherhood; it's when it is excessive that it may be a sign of depression. It is closely bound up with your view of yourself, and so deep feelings of unworthiness are another danger sign. You may feel that no one wants to speak to you, or that they're laughing at you or talking about you behind your back, or ignoring you because you're a failure. You may feel too unattractive to face other people: your hair is horrible, your weight is wrong, even your skin texture is repellant, too dry or too oily. Again, everyone has flashes of feeling like this sometimes, especially in the aftermath of a birth; it is when such feelings dominate how you interact with others that they may be a sign of depression. Sometimes, too, such feelings can grow worse until they become thoughts of suicide. Some women (like Tara in the opening of this chapter) also report feeling nothing at all, numb or dead inside.

Anxiety

Sadly, anxiety can take away much of the contentment of motherhood. Mothers may worry about the health of their baby, another child, their partner, or themselves. One mother remembers feeling worried and guilty after the birth of her first baby because she was more concerned with her own health than anything else.

> Sandra, 31, a nurse, had suffered quite badly with headaches and painful periods before becoming pregnant and had been seeing a homeopath. Now the baby was born, she very much feared a recurrence of symptoms which pregnancy had suspended.
> 'I felt guilty at not being more up when I had a perfect little baby, and aware that I should be thinking more about her, not myself.'

Yet, why shouldn't a mother have some concern for herself – especially if the baby *is* perfect? The mother's displacement by the baby, already touched on in the Introduction, and the vital issue of how much the new mother needs mothering, will both be discussed more fully in chapter 3.

Fears and phobias

Fear can be general, or directed towards particular objects: a fear of spending too much money, that your partner will lose his job or not adapt well to fatherhood, or simply 'free-floating' anxiety, that big black cloud that threatens you don't quite know what. Convinced that 'something is going to happen', you may feel too afraid even to go out, feeling safer alone and at home. Other specific phobias can develop, such as a fear of flying or of going on trains. Occasionally fear can be strikingly focused.

16

Lorraine, 23, was married to a long-distance lorry driver. After having her first baby, she became convinced that he was going to die in a crash, and for two years insisted on the baby and herself accompanying him 'so we can all go together'. Their house was left empty for most of the time, while Lorraine did up the back of the lorry to make it as home-like as possible. A counsellor struggled in vain to cure Lorraine of this fear; eventually it wore away of its own accord.

Eating or drinking disorders

Normal mealtime routines are likely to be disrupted after a baby is born, and a woman who has recently given birth will retain a few extra pounds anyway (nature's way of safeguarding fat supplies for breastfeeding). So, don't worry if your eating isn't too regular. If you're breastfeeding, you will also get hungrier and thirstier than usual. But really compulsive eating or drinking can be signs of depression, as can a total loss of appetite. In general, any dramatic changes in your *attitude* to food or drink can be warning signs, though not changes in preparing food which are forced upon you by the fact that previous cooking time has now become baby time.

Loss of libido

This is a very common symptom, but can make more trouble in a partnership than many other symptoms put together, conjuring the devils of rejection and jealousy in a partner which may already have been awakened by the baby's arrival. This area is where sympathy and support may break down, if not all the time, at least intermittently.

Even apart from post-birth complications like a sore stitch area, a woman involved in one close physical relationship with a baby may just not be able to cope with another. It is as if breastfeeding, cuddling and so on, siphon off all physical interest – nature's way, perhaps, of ensuring the sexual siren does become a mum! This is especially so if you are depressed and your energy level is low.

Although the loss of libido may last longer if you are depressed, sexual energy does return in time, although it may be among the last of the symptoms to lift. Until then, it may simply be a case of waiting with what patience can be mustered. However, it isn't always a case of the importunate man besieging the reluctant woman – men too can suffer from a drop in libido; after all, they too have to adapt to fatherhood. More on men in chapter 7.

2

Understanding Postnatal Depression

Because postnatal depression is not always easy to recognize or define, it helps to know as much as possible about the condition. Being able to assess your own depression intellectually may not always help you to recover, but it may give you enough awareness of what is going on to spur you into seeking help. This chapter looks at some of the background to postnatal depression, as well as other mental postnatal disorders.

Two other types of postnatal illness

There are two other postnatal disorders which need to be distinguished from the main subject of this book, that is, what could be called 'mainstream' postnatal depression as defined in the last chapter. The baby blues and puerperal psychosis have both been loosely classed as 'postnatal depression', although this is really misleading, the one being highly common and transient, the other being extremely rare and much more serious. If you're reading this book, it isn't so likely that you will be suffering either the blues or psychosis. The one is over too soon for long-term information to be necessary, while the other involves a detachment from reality which makes reading a self-help book a fairly fruitless proposition. Nevertheless, it is useful to understand what you're not suffering from, and, in the case of the baby blues, to understand what you may well have experienced soon after the birth. Depression can also sometimes develop from the baby blues.

The baby blues

The baby blues, believed to affect more than half of all women, are usually viewed as 'normal and nothing to worry about'. They are sometimes referred to as 'Day 4 blues', because they so often take place then, though they may equally arrive on the third or fifth day after the birth, or even later. Some women have said theirs were 'delayed' by the constraints of a hospital setting, bursting out a week or so later in the privacy of their own home. Other women value having been able to have a good cry on a supportive nurse's shoulder!

The baby blues are unmistakable, taking the form of what romantic novels usually call a passionate storm of weeping. Such bottomless sorrow can hit you so suddenly as to feel almost physical, and the baby blues have indeed been linked with the hormonal changes that accompany the arrival of your milk; in the nineteenth century, the condition was called the 'milk fever'. You may well run a slight temperature at this time and feel generally uncomfortable, with ballooning breasts, irritating stitches, and visitors who refuse to leave. The blues may last for a couple of hours only, or continue for a few days, but are usually well over by Day 10.

This at any rate is the usual explanation of 'the blues'. They do however need to be seen in context as part of the fluctuating emotions of those early days just after childbirth. Hormones may indeed be fundamental, but surely some violent emotional reaction is allowable after the challenges of pregnancy and the excitement of birth. Perhaps you remember bursting into tears after other stressful events: sitting exams, a hard week at work, a minor car accident. In this sense, the blues can really help assimilate what has happened, indeed 'a good cry' is traditionally regarded as healthy, followed we hope by lots of tea and sympathy. It is when the blues don't pass away that they can progress into postnatal depression, which is why it can be helpful not to dismiss them as unimportant. (More on the significance of the blues in chapter 3.)

Puerperal psychosis

Sometimes described as the most severe end of postnatal depression, puerperal psychosis is usually viewed as a condition apart. Certainly, women already suffering from depression should not fear that they will go on to develop puerperal psychosis. For a start, it should be emphasized that it is extremely rare, although its highly coloured nature means it does get written about perhaps more than its incidence justifies. Also, puerperal psychosis usually strikes very soon after birth, often soon enough for the postnatal nurses to spot it while the mother is still in the ward.

Puerperal psychosis has severe symptoms: the most striking include delusions and visual or auditory hallucinations. The woman might think her baby is a god, or hear voices telling her to give him away or leave him somewhere, or see strange nurses coming to take him away. Manic symptoms of puerperal psychosis include excitement and inflation: a mother may feel all-dominant, her mind racing, her thoughts disjointed and hard to follow. She may be too 'high' to eat or sleep properly, leading to collapse. Tears, tension and panic characterize the depressive symptoms, with the mother simply unable to cope with everyday life, including care of the baby. Her behaviour may be totally irrational to outsiders, though she is driven on by an inner often obsessive logic of her own. Appetite, sleep, libido and social life are all drastically affected, and suicide is a real danger.

This condition needs urgent medical help. Because of this, and because it has been extensively described in other books (see Further Reading), puerperal psychosis will receive little further attention after this section. Treatment includes supportive therapy from a doctor or other professional, often in hospital; these days, mother and baby are kept together as much as possible. Anti-depressant drugs, hormone therapy and ECT (painless) may all help. Other treatments include relaxation classes, group and occupational therapy. After hospital, aftercare includes follow-up by psychiatrists, social workers and health visitors. With such a barrage of treatment, a woman would have to be unfortunate indeed if she did not get well, and the treatment *is* very often quickly effective. The most important point is to make sure that sufferer and treatment do meet up.

'Postnatal depression':
problems with the label

Postnatal depression then could be said to fall between the extremes of the baby blues and of puerperal psychosis. Yet, although 'postnatal depression' sounds as if it refers to one specific disorder, it actually applies to a variety of mental and emotional disturbances in women who have recently had a baby. In fact, this catch-all term gives little real idea of the wide scope of disorders which exist, and there is a tendency to bundle any mental or emotional upsets after childbirth under the heading of postnatal depression. One criticism of this has been that it risks dismissing a whole range of social and emotional or psychological experience under what has been called a 'pseudo-scientific' label. It implies that women who are actually passing through a life experience are merely ill, so diminishing the validity of that experience.

So, how can you tell the difference between the changes every woman experiences after having a baby, and true postnatal depression? Is it a question of degree or of kind? Or has the label achieved the renown it has because it dignifies the universal experience, touching on a profound truth about every woman's adaptation to becoming a mother? The varying experiences of the women interviewed for this book have provided touchstones in this area, and one of the conclusions is that, even if all mothers have to go through the adaptation process, depression after birth certainly hits some harder than others.

Jenny, an art teacher who had her first baby at 29, was fully aware of the difficulties that early parenthood can bring while not being fully convinced of the validity of postnatal depression as a label to describe what happened to her.

'Shall we say that I found having a baby challenging! I don't know if I did have postnatal depression. I've read a bit about it and other women's experiences seem so much worse than mine, yet I did find it all difficult. It was a great shock to find myself tied to a tiny baby, to have lost my freedom. There were several ghastly nights when the baby would wake up five or six times and I wondered how I could go on. I was extremely tired and seemed to get ill quite a lot. It seemed to be such a lone struggle. My husband was made redundant and we were short of money and very anxious. We wanted to move house. There was definitely a point around a year after the birth when we suddenly looked up and felt we'd come through the wall at last.'

Jenny's story highlights the point that ordinary reactions to having a birth can merge into depression; also, that common life problems like redundancy and housing are worsened by having the new responsibility of a child. It also shows how sometimes a combination of points can sometimes make for depression, and, in this way, acts as a warning against trying to define postnatal depression too rigidly. Indeed, some researchers have spoken of the need to subdivide postnatal depression into at least five categories before the labels can be at all meaningful.

Meanwhile, it can be argued that the label does dignify women's experiences after birth; it at least indicates *some* awareness of the emotional problems which can arise after childbirth. Our present-day recognition of postnatal depression is after all fairly recent and research is still young. We do live in a society of the quick label, with recognition of a wide range of problems: you can be anything from co-dependent to a compulsive gambler. Indeed, some complain that you are left out if you *don't* have a problem, but, in a society where geographical and cultural certainties such as the village and the neighbour have broken down, people do need to create their own communities according to common need. Labels have a use, and would not emerge if there wasn't a need for them: they give status to people grappling for meaning, a valuable working standpoint from which to re-create identity and society on their own terms.

Tara was depressed for four months before hearing the words 'postnatal depression'. She was immensely relieved to find that all those vague, inchoate feelings of misery meant something, that they did amount to a recognizable condition. For her, being able to name the problem was halfway towards solving it.

In addition – important with postnatal depression – a strong label gives a handle on understanding to families and friends. It is much easier for those around a depressed woman to help her if they can think of her as suffering from an illness, even though postnatal depression is not known to be directly caused by a virus or bacteria (depression can sometimes follow an illness such as flu of course and postnatal depression may sometimes occur this way). In the multifarious nature of postnatal depression, disease remains a useful metaphor. Of course, problems with the label are closely linked with the causes of postnatal depression, discussed in the following section.

Postnatal depression: background and possible causes

Although our own awareness of postnatal depression is so recent, the problem was first mentioned by the great Greek doctor Hippocrates in the fourth century BCE, who was known, appropriately, as the 'father of medicine'. After this, although there was a subdued kind of awareness that a woman with a baby might sometimes behave a bit oddly, little serious medical attention was given to postnatal depression. One probable reason for this is that people were much more alarmed about infection after delivery (puerperal pyrexia), which was often fatal. It is only in the last half century or so that this danger has passed with the advance of modern antibiotics.

Another historical landmark came in the mid-nineteenth century with the French physician Louis Marcé, whose research marked the beginnings of real scientific interest in the problem. Adopting his name, the Marcé Society was founded in 1980 and the Association for Postnatal Illness around the same time, in the face of much ignorance about postnatal depression, and much need for more knowledge and support. Over the past few years, these groups have gone a long way towards making postnatal depression better understood, and there are other support groups for mothers where depression will be accepted and understood.

Much of the impetus for research has also come from the medical profession. For example, work at Edinburgh University resulted in a special questionnaire to help health professionals assess whether a woman is suffering from postnatal depression. Dr Katherine Dalton is well known for many years of research into the hormonal aspects of postnatal depression. Dr Brice Pitt has researched and written extensively from the psychiatric viewpoint. A preliminary study at Dulwich Hospital, London, has explored the impact of further hormonal treatment.

In other words, postnatal depression has been the subject of serious research, even if it remains a complex subject with many more avenues for exploration. So, don't be afraid that what you are suffering is 'nothing' or not worthy of attention – some of the best minds in the country have given years to the study of postnatal depression.

A figure often heard is that 10 per cent of all women suffer from postnatal depression, and this does mean all women. As far as can be ascertained, it seems that the same figure applies to other societies, with differing family and social structures. An African survey for example also backed up the 10 per cent figure. Does this mean that 10 per cent of women simply find childrearing harder than the other 90 per cent, or that they are suffering from a real, measurable psychiatric or physical condition? The answers differ. Some believe that postnatal depression is no different from any other type of depression, and should be treated accordingly. Others say it is a disorder apart, not typical of other depressions, with certain differentiating symptoms. Broadly speaking, however, experts tend to believe that postnatal depression is caused either by the physical aspects of pregnancy and birth, or by the psychological and/or social stresses of becoming a mother – definitions which would seem to leave depression open to a potentially much wider number than the classic 10 per cent.

Many women have spoken of a cycle of events which led to their depression, rather than just one cause. Lucy was one of them:

'My thinking on what happened has come full circle. I used to think my depression had been purely chemical but it brought up too many things, such as the death of my father when I was in my teens, which I'd never really grieved over. I'm sure birth acted as a trigger for all those feelings of loss to come out. I'm also convinced that physical factors played a part – for example, I was very depleted after suffering badly from vomiting in pregnancy. And the depression certainly took off when my doctor put me back on the pill. I'm sure my hormones were in a mess. But so many other factors played a part – the fact that my baby was born with clicky hips and had a badly fitted harness, that she wanted to feed all the time and I didn't seem to have enough milk, my own high expectations of life, being at home after having a high-powered career, Catholic guilt – it's very complex.'

When you're still stuck in the depression, you may not find it so helpful to worry out whether it's a clinical or spiritual disorder or both. More important is the recognition that treatment of the whole person may be required, involving some reassessment of life, and anyway needing more help than either the statement, 'Pull yourself together, it's all the mind', or, 'Don't worry, it's only your hormones.'

Who is prone to postnatal depression?

Is there a postnatal depressive type? Some would seem to be obvious candidates – those who have had emotional or mental troubles before, those who have real life stresses such as lack of money, poor housing or being a single parent, who may be chronically depressed. It is by no means given that just because you fall into any of these categories, you must suffer from postnatal depression. But these groups, along with some others, have been pin-pointed as being especially vulnerable to the dangers of depression.

Yet again, the broad nature of postnatal depression is reflected by the different factors which can make it more likely: if your own mother suffered from it, if you have severe pre-menstrual tension, if you have had a previous abortion or miscarriage. A difficult birth and feeding difficulties afterwards have also been cited as triggers to postnatal depression. Support around the time of the birth is also important, especially from your own mother or a mother figure, and not enough of this kind of support may contribute to depression. Women who have had infertility treatment in order to become pregnant are more likely to suffer, it is thought because their expectations of parenthood are higher – hardly surprising in view of the stress and time usually involved in such treatment.

Other risk factors have been investigated, such as a difficult or anxious pregnancy in which a partner wasn't as understanding or supportive as hoped. The grounds for depression can also be laid further back in your life: any kind of childhood trauma can underlie depression. More specifically, a problematic relationship with your own mother in childhood can lie behind postnatal depression.

Is postnatal depression more likely to occur with a first baby or with subsequent ones? Experience differs: some women have depression only with a first or with a second baby, others with their first and third babies but not the second one, and so on. In other words, it can be quite unpredictable. Some women are deeply shaken by their first contact with birth and babycare; some can manage one child well enough but are struck by a dramatic loss of freedom when the second one comes along; some experience this reaction after a third child. Others find the fourth child difficult, again because three is a more manageable unit than four – perhaps too because four is so much further off the social two-child norm. One study however has indicated that depression is most common in first pregnancies, closely followed by second ones. In third pregnancies, the depression declined by around half, and declined still further in terminated pregnancies (for more on interrupted pregnancies, see below under 'Postnatal depression after a terminated pregnancy'). Fourth pregnancies come last of all.

What about the possibility of postnatal depression recurring from pregnancy to pregnancy? Another study put the rate of recurrence at well over 50 per cent, although some women do choose not to have another child after their first experience. Certainly, those who have had postnatal depression before are cited as being especially vulnerable to having it again.

This brings us on to the next point: could postnatal depression be prevented? It has been suggested that prevention could form part of routine antenatal care, perhaps by means of a simple questionnaire between GP and patient. This would of course be easier in subsequent pregnancies, but you can certainly take it upon yourself to mention a former depression to your doctor if you become pregnant again, and to discuss any fears of a recurrence. It has also been suggested (by women who have been through postnatal depression) that midwives play a bigger part in spotting budding depression, by making one or two extra visits a few weeks after the birth, because they are not perceived as as threatening as health visitors and/or social workers. The suggestion certainly shows that there is room for more actively supportive professional care and that some women, notably those who have been through postnatal depression once, would like to see more of this kind of care before the birth, as well as after.

Your age at delivery

Age in itself has not really been a proven factor in whether you are more or less likely to develop postnatal depression. Nevertheless, you may find it helpful to look at the different pressures younger and older mothers are under, as these may contribute to depression.

These days, more and more women are leaving it later to have a baby (28 is the average, though many women wait a few years later than this). With the advantage of more maturity and tolerance, and a more settled lifestyle, older women are also that much more used to being in charge, to being able to manage their own lives, an attitude which can make depression more likely when it doesn't carry over into babycare. The high-powered career woman who has her baby and returns to work within ten days is a myth which seems to have a particular grip on our society's imagination, and while this may suit a few individuals, it is unrealistic for many more. Yet, older working women especially may find it particularly hard to let go of this organizing attitude when looking after a baby. They think they *ought* to be able to manage, and when the baby wears them down by irregular or constant feeds, crying, no schedule and little sleep, such women may be much more prone to depression.

This is only part of the general higher expectations held by older mothers, often used to a better standard of living than younger ones. In practical terms, this may mean giving themselves more to do after the birth because standards of cleanliness and tidiness have to be kept up. But it is the physical demands of babycare which can be so wearing to older mothers.

> Carrie, who had her first baby at 35, blamed her depression on the sheer hard work of babycare. Whereas ten years before she had been able to hold down a demanding job and socialize for half the night with no problems, she was now 'wiped out' by her baby's night wakings, breastfeeding, and the fact that she barely had a moment to herself.

What about younger mothers? While they may be more adaptable, less set in their ways and with more physical energy, they may not have as much patience or maturity as older women who have waited to have a child. They may be more liable to feel that they're missing out on part of their youth, or that they're giving up a career which is barely established, sometimes only just started. Both of these feelings may entail a kind of grieving which can play its part in depression.

Postnatal depression after a terminated pregnancy

Emotional reactions after a miscarriage or abortion can be quite as strong as after a live birth. Antonia, a photographer, had postnatal depression when she was 29 after the birth of her first child, but believes she already suffered when in her early twenties she had an abortion after accidentally becoming pregnant.

> 'For about a year afterwards I went round – I can only describe it as mad. I didn't tell anyone about it because I didn't really realize what it was and I didn't think anyone would be able to help. In the end, just as I was coming out of it, I did go to my doctor and they told me it sounded just like postnatal depression.'

Obviously, the reactions are not going to be exactly the same when there is no baby. But the danger of depression after a termination should not be underestimated; it can be a highly traumatic event which demands a certain amount of grieving. For more information about emotional reaction after losing a baby in pregnancy, you might find another Sheldon title of help: *Talking about miscarriage* by Sarah Murphy.

Good and bad days

The course of depression does not run smooth. While there may be days on end when you feel too paralysed to cope with life, there may also come days when you feel better: days when the baby succeeds in charming you out of it for a while, or you curl up on the sofa with a book or TV and, letting go of all those draining anxieties, reach some quiet equilibrium of your own.

Cherish such moments. Don't allow them to be spoiled by guilt or the haunting feeling that you should be doing something else. Write down your feelings on good days, and read them on bad ones. And rest assured that the good days will increase in number and in quality. Just because they are followed by bad days for now doesn't mean the bad days are going to win in the end.

3

The Myth of the
Perfect Birth

'I remember being depressed because the birth had been so traumatic. When the weekly anniversary came round I would cry around
the time I'd given birth, because I couldn't forget the pain. That did
wear off quite quickly, though – after the first six weeks or so.'

Jenny explicitly links her birth experience to her feelings afterwards,
although in general she wasn't sure if what she went through could be
called depression or not. So, what happens when birth doesn't go to
plan? When what happened was so different from what you expected
that it can leave an emotional scar? A difficult labour may not actually
cause depression, but many women feel that it predisposed them to it, or
tipped the balance among other factors such as poverty or isolation. For
some this was a matter of physical factors such as not being allowed to eat
in labour, and so ending up drained, or not being able to sleep because of
constant monitoring. Others felt guilty and not good enough because of
the way they had coped with pain or the progress of labour. If what
happens is very different from what you expected, a longer-lasting
depression can result (i.e. not just the baby blues). Just fifty years ago,
some women still went into birth not knowing the physical facts of how
the baby was going to be born, and you may even come across the odd
grandmother now who will admit as much.

Iris, in her mid-seventies, looked back to the birth of her first child at
18:

'I had no idea what was going to happen. I thought I'd just go to
hospital, they'd give me something to make me unconscious, and I'd
be handed a nice little baby. It took me years to get over what
happened.'

Of course this kind of ignorance is rare now, but even in these days of
bean bags, breathing and water births, it is still possible not to realize the
totally demanding nature of a birth before it happens, to be unprepared
for pain, for a long labour, or for an emergency caesarean. There is little
doubt that a bad birth can make for a shaky start to motherhood, and that
some people take longer to get over it than others; and that the stress of it
can act as a trigger for problems to emerge. It is certainly worth going

28

over your own birth experience to see if that's where the roots of your depression lie. Was it a disappointment or a shock in some way? Did you feel inadequate or powerless? Was your image of yourself as a coping person shaken? Was it very draining physically? Birth is the dividing point between your vision of yourself as a mother and the reality, and it's important to recognize that the gap between the two can sometimes be a starting point for depression, with or without other contributing factors.

Expectations of birth

To say that our expectations of birth are still very high is only to give the end result of a whole social process. That is to say, there is an immense amount of labour (so to speak) by all sorts of people towards the moment of birth. As soon as you officially declare yourself pregnant, a small army of people is there to help you towards delivery: doctors, midwives, antenatal teachers, anaesthesists, nurses and so on.

The whole antenatal process, with the focus on delivery, can't help but raise expectations of the birth, expectations which can easily bear the seeds of depression when it proves hard or painful. You may not have realized that your hopes are perhaps different from those of everyone in the antenatal machine. The paramount aim of doctors and their colleagues is a safe delivery. With huge maternal mortality rates a thing of the past, most pregnant women haven't inherited the medical memory doctors have to carry round with them: before modern obstetrics, birth *could* be dangerous. Of course you too hope for a safe delivery! It's just that, for various reasons, your expectations of birth may be unrealistically high.

The attitude of many women today is an often unconscious tribute to medical progress; because birth is so safe these days, ideas of it have risen above safety. It is perhaps only in our day that we have the luxury of wondering whether birth will offer personal challenge and fulfilment, and whether pethidine or an epidural would most nearly match our moral or spiritual stance. It didn't used to be so, as any reasonably honest grandmother will tell you!

Birth – fear of failure

The gap then between the idealistic and realistic views of birth can be one starting place for depression. When birth isn't the sublime personal experience, but prolonged, messy and perhaps touched with danger, it can be so easy to feel that you have 'failed'. One mother described birth as 'an exam which women are under pressure to pass'.

Sandra became quite obsessed with her 'bad birth' and would repeat the story over and over again to anyone who would listen. Even later, when she'd recovered, she couldn't help seeing the problem as one of a lack of strength which she *ought* somehow to have commanded, even though rationally she knew she needn't feel like that.

'To be challenged at such depth – and not to have the inner resources to meet that challenge – leaves you very shaken and guilty. Even though I've got a much more balanced view now, I still sometimes catch myself thinking, you should have done better.'

It isn't even a question of what sort of baby we will succeed in producing, central though this concern is. It is the birth process: how will we do during the birth? Will we get the better of it, will we win? Or will that unknown quantity, the pain, dominate us? Will the medical staff impose their will on us? Behind much of our thinking about the birth experience lies not so much fear of the unknown as the issue of control – an interesting point because one feature of postnatal depression is the feeling of being *out* of control, of not being able to cope.

The fact that birth takes place whether you like it or not may be quite successfully side-stepped by such thinking, which does its best to act as a control mechanism in a situation where (apart from inductions or caesareans) not that much control is possible. No one really knows what triggers the hormonal fall which results in labour. In fact, throughout the whole pregnancy/birth process, your most powerful moment is choosing to become pregnant (although even this doesn't ensure the desired outcome). After that, although you need to practise preventative care such as not smoking or drinking, you quickly reach the limits of your power to control the progress and outcome of your pregnancy.

Birth, it would seem, offers a chance to redress this, to control the event with breathing techniques, drug choice and birth position. But when it actually happens, it can come as a shock to realize that it is your body which is having the baby, not you, and that your body will have the baby no matter what. This certainly isn't to disparage breathing techniques and so on, of course your own attitude helps. It is just that many women don't realize, until it happens, how limited their power is during this huge physical onslaught – 'My body took over' is a typical comment. And for some women, being out of control can be a deeply frightening experience whose emotional effects colour much of their first few months with their baby.

Antenatal classes –
do they really prepare you?

It's a fairly common complaint that antenatal preparation focuses too much on birth, with little or no talk of how to cope emotionally or practically afterwards. But many women's birth experience puts this complaint in new focus: they feel they weren't prepared for the birth itself; they weren't prepared for its violence, its unpredictable rhythms, or all the individual fallings-off from textbook procedure which take place so much more often than may be realized. The result can be feelings of resentment and alienation which may progress into postnatal depression.

The wide range of reactions to birth among different women does make it difficult to anticipate individual ones, and there's the ever-present danger of 'putting ideas in people's heads', the fear that talking about feelings might help create them where otherwise they wouldn't have existed. But if you went into labour reasonably hopeful and confident, and found that the reality challenged you beyond your strength, you may feel cheated and disappointed. Why didn't someone at least warn you? In fact, some antenatal classes *do* talk about birth in a realistic way; they also talk about postnatal depression. The problem is that chat about a difficult birth and/or depression usually isn't what the listeners want to hear; it doesn't fit in with the hopeful personal myth of childbirth women are encouraged to have while pregnant. As Pam, an antenatal instructor describes:

'You can see the eyes glazing over – when I say that out of everyone sitting in this room one in ten is likely to suffer from depression, they always think it won't happen to them. The men take it in more.'

There is in any case a vast difference between hearing about something and living through it. Isn't it rather the same with any new experience, from starting a new job to flying for the first time? You may be prepared for it *ad nauseam* yet still find, when it happens, that there are a host of things which 'nobody told me'. Antenatal classes can only do so much, on all aspects of birth and babycare: keeping a new baby clean on a day to day basis is very different from watching an expert midwife give this week's demonstration baby his first bath.

Labour pain – a last taboo?

So, what exactly is it about birth which so traumatizes some women? Although some women take it in their stride, labour pain is for many women *the* big shock of giving birth. 'Unbearable.' 'I never imagined anything could hurt so much.' 'No one tells you a thing about it.' These are typical comments and it is with the last that this section is concerned, because of the effects of pain which may last beyond the birth. *Does* no one tell you? The pregnant woman has traditionally been subject to numerous taboos, such as not being allowed to look at the moon, or at a dead person, or even to get upset, in case it harmed her unborn baby. Today, for a society in which so many taboos have broken down, there are indications that this awe of the pregnant woman, one of the most ancient in the world, still holds good. Is the fairly guarded silence about pain during labour part of this? People *are* cautious of mentioning the possibility of pain to a pregnant woman, for all sorts of good reasons: pain is subjective and varies from person to person; some women hardly feel pain at all; talking about pain will implant fear in the woman leading to more pain. The result is that many women are absolutely taken aback by the intensity of labour pain, and may not find that, as commonly stated, 'you forget it all the minute the baby arrives'.

Indeed, as Jenny's opening quote shows, the memory of the pain alone can be enough to cause depression of a kind. And for some women, the other common remark, 'Never again', becomes a reality. Sadly, some women do decide not to have any more children because of their birth experience – a 'failure' which is cause enough for depression, especially if they might otherwise have liked more children.

Perhaps however it isn't really fair to call a certain hedging round the subject of pain a 'conspiracy of silence', as some women have. As said above, some antenatal classes do talk outright about pain; books and magazine articles are also more open about it, taking, however, good care to emphasize how much the experience of pain varies from person to person. But openness can't always be the answer when dealing with this problem, as Pam again explains:

'I used to talk openly about pain, and to say quite frankly, labour hurts. After all, what do you think pain relief is *for*? Now I don't bother, for the simple reason that the women don't listen. You can see they just don't want to know. When it does happen to them, they think they're the only ones in the world who got it wrong until they start talking to other mums.'

Even women who've been through labour find themselves caught by the remaining links of this taboo of not alarming the pregnant woman. Jenny, who found labour pain 'unbelievable', nevertheless didn't want her experience to corrode someone else's birth.

'It's the old dilemma – do you tell a pregnant friend how painful labour is or not? You don't want to alarm them and spoil their pregnancy. I tend to keep quiet.'

On a pragmatic note, there really shouldn't be any need to allow fear of pain to prevent another pregnancy. It is always possible to discuss pain relief options with your doctor next time round and some women do book epidurals not for strict medical reasons but simply because they choose not to put themselves through pain.

'Pregnancy hormones may play havoc with your moods'

'But don't worry, this is quite normal!' So runs typical advice which skims over the emotional changes which take place during pregnancy. Apart from any lingering taboos, the emotional area of pregnancy is subject to a certain amount of stereotypical, at times contradictory, thinking. If the old wives' tales outlined above form a fairly crude recognition that the pregnant woman is a special case, perhaps another parallel could be said to come from the world of classical myth, where sacrificial kings are fêted and pampered for a year before being slaughtered!

The pregnant woman is traditionally regarded as especially vulnerable, in need of special diet and protection, a delicate flower somehow apart from the stormy realities of life. She's seen as a creature of strange moods and whims, victim to tears and cravings, a driven being who thinks nothing of sending her partner out on a cold night to search for lemonade or ice cream. She's regarded as being too occupied with new growth to have room for negative emotions, wholly occupied with the burgeoning life inside her.

The problem with these stereotypes is that they allow for all sorts of freak feelings during pregnancy without at the same time acknowledging any need to take them too seriously. In some respects, the social isolation of the mother begins with this kind of thinking. For example, vivid, sometimes alarming dreams are a well-known feature of pregnancy – dreams of not being able to cope, of forgetting the baby in a shop, of having a deformed, miniature baby. It would certainly be helpful to discuss such fears of coping while still pregnant, given that postnatal depression is so concerned with *not* coping. 'Mood swings' can be mornings spent in deep gloom, or bouts of anguished secret crying reported by some women, or even violent anger. While this may also be due to hormonal causes, sorting out psychological conflicts during pregnancy might again be helpful in lessening the chances of depression afterwards.

An especially relevant point here is ambivalence about wanting a child at all. The feelings of being out of control during birth, and out of control in depression, can sometimes be a continuing link with feelings about pregnancy. There is the sometimes frightening realization that the baby grows without you being able to do anything about it, that the only way out is through birth. There is also the social pressure to want a child wholeheartedly, with no shades of desire, a task which is really as hard as being a round-the-clock mother. As you will see if you read on, these kinds of social expectations, starting in pregnancy, also play a large part in creating depression after the birth.

Another point is important physically and concerns how some women more or less refuse to admit they're pregnant. This isn't the hearty soul who goes on working up to the day before labour because she enjoys it. It is the woman who feels anxious and guilty if she is more tired than usual, who fights a running battle with her body all through pregnancy, refusing to rest and expecting more of herself than she is physically capable of. When pushed into early childcare, this attitude is a danger because an over-tired mother so easily becomes a depressed one. Many women do put pressure on themselves during pregnancy by feeling they 'should' be doing more, yet it is important to realize that even the most capable woman can be knocked out by the physical processes of pregnancy. The side-effects of pregnancy – sometimes actual illness – can leave you physically weakened and so also more prone to depression.

With all this in mind, it might be helpful to think back to your pregnancy, to your feelings, any depression you felt then, and to try and see how your pregnancy and birth fitted together, whether tensions from pregnancy were carried through into labour, whether you were physically tired out from pregnancy before labour even began. Try writing this down and comparing it with a diary kept of your postnatal depression, to see if the same themes emerge. You might not find a pattern but the chances are that it will clear your head of any remaining feelings about the birth, and clarify any carried-over conflicts which may be contributing to your present depression.

4

Becoming a Mother:
Loss and Change
after Childbirth

'My baby was born at Christmas time. I'll never forget how melancholy the carols sounded, all celebrating a birth that was going to end in death on the cross. They all seemed full of a mother's sorrow, her grief that her baby's birth ultimately means death. This was the origin of my depression. I thought that Mary's sadness was the grief of all women who have babies. Oh, and I hated the flowers in the ward – they seemed like so many funeral bouquets.'

For Lucy, her words marked the start of a period of grief after childbirth. Her vision may seem unjustifiably sombre, but does show how the conventional view of the joyous mother can have a dark undertow. The gift of new life is precious, yet if you're depressed you may not be able to feel this because morbid thoughts take over.

Becoming a mother is not just a matter of simple joy at the arrival of a baby. It is an event which involves inner change on a deep level, and the psychological stresses in this are considered by one school of thought to be a major cause of postnatal depression. Motherhood means shedding a whole past identity: the woman who is wheeled into the postnatal ward is already not the same as the one who, some hours earlier, presented at the labour ward. The (sometimes ambivalent) happiness and hope of pregnancy behind you, the thrill and shock of birth over, there follows a period of adjustment where disappointment or even grief may play a part in your depression.

Why, when having a baby is supposed to be a positive event? One answer is that motherhood does involve loss as well as gain. It means coming to terms with the fact that one way of life is over: your own childhood, your youth (in the sense of irresponsibility rather than age), and your freedom, at least to some extent. While Lucy's words focus on the mortality of the child, birth really means the death of one self for the mother – the self she has always known. And, if it also means the coming to birth of another self, this process is for some perhaps no less painful than actual childbirth. Adapting to motherhood can take a lot of energy, too, and if you're exhausted by birth and early childcare, the combination of these factors may tip you into depression.

This vulnerable time, when one self has passed away and another isn't fully born, has been dubbed 'birthshock' or 'babyshock'. It is the shock of having to care all the time for a tiny, unpredictable, even alien being; of being totally committed, of having your own needs thoroughly and ruthlessly put second place. For some women, it can be devastating to realize how tied they are, how utterly their freedom has gone. As Marcia recalls:

'I remember crying with helplessness that I couldn't do anything – have a bath or a coffee or get dressed or anything, without this infant wanting me every five seconds. To be really blunt, I suffered terribly from constipation after the birth and I couldn't seem to get rid of it and every time I sat on the loo the baby would start crying and I'd be in agony! In the end I sort of gave up. I got very depressed and just rather hated the child in a sullen sort of way, gave up even trying to get dressed and all that. Then one day I thought, well, it isn't the poor little thing's fault, she didn't ask to be born. It got better when she was around three months old – she stopped being quite so demanding, and by then I was much more relaxed with her. And now of course, two years later, I couldn't imagine life without her!'

As this quote shows, this initial realization of being tied sinks in not just during the hours and weeks after birth, but over months. And while major adjustment does take place during the first three months, 'birthshock' may last even longer. Certainly you shouldn't put pressure on yourself to adapt before you comfortably can – many women need as much as a year just in which to build up a sense of a new identity. As Marcia's words show, the realization that you've lost your freedom can be a great psychological burden which for some is just too heavy, sinking them into depression. But as she also points out there is a breakthrough point, sooner for some, later for others, when it's suddenly more possible to accept the presence of another tiny person around.

It is at times difficult to talk about this process of change without sounding negative. For a start, you don't want to imply that, just because you've had a baby, you *have* to be depressed. Also, while in moments of rage or despair you might feel you don't deserve to be a mother, or would have been better off never having had the baby, few women would really choose to go back to their pre-baby days even if they could. Already the baby has made too huge an impact. It is one of parenthood's mysteries how life soon becomes unthinkable without this small person who, a short while previously, just wasn't there. Having a baby remains a privilege, a life event which can challenge you into a new sense of maturity, which is much more elastic in accepting change and growth in the self. Losing your old self can also mean finding it again in the reliving of your childhood which takes place as your baby grows older and brings back memories of your own past. It isn't always possible to see all this while in the depression, which can act as a kind of grey blanket, veiling insights and hopes for the future alike. It is only when the depression lifts and you look back that you may be surprised at how much more you can see.

The reality of motherhood

Being on 24-hour call is one of the hardest things for new mothers to get used to. It's the feeling that, in the last issue, there's nobody else to take the baby, especially if you're breastfeeding. A father can 'help', as can perhaps relatives and friends, but no matter how adorable that baby is yours, and he's there all the time. Certainly being left alone with a baby is a situation which can have more than a touch of nightmare, as Suzanne describes:

'Those long winter nights! Because I was breastfeeding, my hormones were still playing tricks on me, so I'd get these hot flushes and get out of bed sweating, as if I'd got a temperature. It was all rather like being ill when you're a child – huge shadows on the walls from the baby's night light, not knowing when you'd be able to go back to sleep, dying to go back to sleep. In the day, I continually felt fluey from lack of sleep – light-headed and achey.'

It's interesting that Suzanne saw getting up at night in terms of illness – that it reminded her especially of childhood illness, a time when you are looked after, rather than doing the looking after. The impossibility of returning to that state is certainly rubbed in by having to get up at night, especially after a birth, and especially if you don't feel too well (something which many mothers complain of in depression). If you are one of the many depressed mothers who hate being left alone with the baby, do try and make arrangements to have company whenever possible. If you're breastfeeding, try and get your partner to bring you the baby at least on alternate nights, so you don't have to get up and so that his involvement makes you feel less alone.

Not being able to take time off even if you are ill remains a hard part of motherhood, but it's important to remember that it isn't impossible. It may take more organization and inconvenience to others, but making sure you do get more rest when you need it can be done. The problem is when you get into a habit of believing that your own needs can't be met, that it isn't worth trying. This kind of low self-worth, a classic component of depression, may need to be tackled before you can ask for help. Start by pampering yourself as much as possible: resting when the baby sleeps, eating properly, and so on. Giving care to yourself makes it easier to accept help from others, as well as being a valuable exercise in quelling the depression even if it's only for a while. In other words, if a nice warm bath makes you feel better for half an hour, have one!

Ignorance about babies

All in all, the reality of the baby can be quite raw, the more so because many women have no experience of babies before having their own. It is quite possible to have your own baby without ever having seen a newborn baby or one of a few days old, because at this age they are usually in hospital or at home. When you do see babies, in the street or on television, they tend to be older, smiling, perhaps mobile. When you have your own, the constant breastfeeding and waking up at night, perhaps constant crying, are all in striking contrast to popular images of babies. There's also the fact that, for the first few weeks at least, you may not be too sure what the baby should be doing in terms of eating and sleeping. Should he be feeding every hour? Is it normal for him to be awake for 50 minutes at a stretch – aren't newborns supposed to sleep all the time? Even if you've had a baby before, this can be a frightening time, because you may have forgotten what it was like, or because an extra baby means the pressure of extra responsibilities in an already-crowded lifestyle.

It is important to realize that you are not the only person to whom a baby is something completely new. Part of depression is this feeling of total isolation, that you are the only one who feels frightened with her baby, not quite sure how to feed or comfort her. Carrie's words could speak for many:

'I knew nothing about babies – I was completely at a loss as to what to do when she cried, and she cried often. She'd catnap on my shoulder for 20 minutes and then wake, crying, wanting to be fed. I could hardly put her down for months. And no one told me that new babies fill their nappies so often, and bring their milk back up, and that you spend half the day changing them and trying to keep them clean. I found the days absolutely exhausting, mentally and physically – endlessly working and getting absolutely nowhere. There was no way I could have cleaned the house. The old cliché about your husband getting home to find you still in your dressing gown – it was true for me. Oh, it was hard work!'

Hard work – does it help then if you can just accept that some babies are the hardest taskmasters you will ever have? This work metaphor is frequently extended to the baby, causing great frustration and also showing how deeply embedded is the work ethic in our society's consciousness. The job never gets finished; it's routine and repetitive, with little mental stimulation; there are no deadlines, no rewards, no feedback, no pay, no time off or holidays. Yet, babies aren't jobs. The words we use can show how irrelevant are many of our expectations of babies, even though those expectations may cause or contribute to depression. Antonia, a photographer, even eventually found she was grateful to her depression for making her lose these expectations.

'The baby challenged my assumptions – all of them; that my time was my own and important, that I had the right to achieve, that life only meant success, or failure. It was like someone putting a big hand in front of my face and saying, "Hey – slow down".'

Loss of fantasy baby

Having a real baby at last, after months of waiting, inevitably means saying goodbye to the fantasy or imaginary baby you carried throughout pregnancy. The gap between what was expected and what arrives is often one reason why it can take time to bond with your baby, and, if you don't fall in love with your baby at first sight, this may start up all sorts of guilt feelings about your value as a mother. It is the impact of arrival: the fact that the baby is undeniably there, warm, maybe wet, putting its tongue out and making tiny noises long before it can actually talk.

Especially if this is your first baby, you may be taken aback by how active and determined even a newborn is, our image of babies leading us to expect sometimes a more totally passive bundle than actually appears. Not having the 'right' feelings towards your baby is part of postnatal depression for some women – some dislike the baby, some feel blank – but try not to make too much of this. Historically, in other cultures, when people had many more children, mothers were often more matter-of-fact about their babies. Instant bonding may be one of the buzzwords of our time, but isn't always realistic. Give yourself time to get to know your new baby.

Another part of saying goodbye to your fantasy baby is that the real one may look different from what you anticipated.

Tara had had an inner picture of a little boy like her partner, with blond hair and blue eyes; she had a dark-haired little girl. Suzanne was convinced that her second baby was going to be a dainty little girl; she had another large boy.

Disappointment about the sex of the baby usually takes precedence over disappointment about looks, though not everyone likes admitting as much. More subtle than this is just the sense that the person who has turned up is not quite the same as you'd imagined, rather like meeting a pen friend for the first time. Some parents give their unborn baby a pet name during pregnancy, and of course some sort of character is built up around this. When you've spent a few months thinking of how strongly Sam is kicking, and what a rumbustious little lad he's going to be, it is strange to find yourself landed with an undeniably strong-willed little girl who alternates periods of noise and quiet – in short, a real person. The strong personality of your average baby soon wipes away the image of the fantasy baby, but may leave its parents temporarily a little bewildered in its wake.

Occasionally a really depressed woman may rebel against what she's been given, allowing a boy's hair to grow long, dressing a girl as a boy, and so on. This deeper conflict may well need counselling or psychiatric care to resolve.

Looking ahead, if your depression lasts for a few months – and sometimes even without depression – it is possible to experience continued disappointment as your baby grows into toddlerhood, again because of the gap between fantasy and reality. What this boils down to is expecting your growing child to be impossibly good, and there can be a feeling that the child who refuses to sleep through the night or has tantrums has let you down. This also has to do with competitive feelings in parenthood – everyone else's children so often seem to behave better: they don't. It is all too easy to expect too much of a tiny child in terms of rational behaviour, and to forget that it is part of a parent's 'job' to set limits. Anger at yourself and at the child can then build up, fuelling depression. Taking responsibility, using this power, can sometimes help solve a behaviour 'problem' and start to break a depression at the same time, although you may need help from a doctor, health visitor or other professional in order to achieve your goals.

The first few days

'I never invite anyone to tea or anything until the baby is six weeks old – I feel they aren't really themselves again until then.'

These words from a mother do give a hint of the nature of that initial period of time spent with a new baby. Chapter 1 has already looked at the 'baby blues', and the tendency to dismiss them as normal and relatively unimportant. Yet surely the emotions of the first few days after birth merit a closer look, whether they progress into full-blown depression or not.

That women weep after giving birth is regarded as normal, even healthy. But the blues, even with hormonal factors to urge them on, can be seen as the first sign of realization that you now have a new life, even the first manifestation of grief for a past which, with the baby's arrival, is irrevocably gone. It is worth looking at what women are weeping *about*.

Marcia spent an afternoon crying over old letters she and her partner had written to each other, with a poignant sense that their time together as a couple was over. Tara was overwhelmed by the feeling that she had made the wrong choice in having a baby, that she was stuck irrevocably on the wrong road, with wasted time and wasted youth behind her. Lucy cried in sheer helplessness and guilt: she felt that she should never have brought a baby into the world, that she'd never be able to look after him.

These are all valid concerns, if exaggerated by the emotions (or the hormones) of the moment. A baby does mean changes in the relationship with a partner, and is a responsibility to bring pause to the most thoughtless. If the full significance of having a child were really to be felt, the baby blues are surely an acceptable reaction.

It might be helpful to write down what you can remember of your own baby blues – how long they lasted, what you were upset about. Perhaps this will give an insight into any concerns underlying your depression which can then be talked through with your doctor, counsellor or friends.

Grief over childhood, youth and freedom

Grieving over your own past childhood and adolescence is a particular part of the psychological process of adapting to motherhood. The poignant feelings of loss, of time passing, do serve some purpose, in that they bring home the reality of what has happened and help you adapt to your new role. Also, paradoxically, part of these feelings of loss can be grasping the essence of your childhood for the first time in years, even before the baby reaches an age at which you can remember yourself as a child. One touching as well as comic manifestation of this is the way new fathers especially will go out and buy a tiny baby all sorts of toys – footballs, rocking horses, books – which he won't be able to enjoy for ages! Some mothers find that these memories of childhood start surfacing during pregnancy, or may continue for some months after the birth.

Tara felt that her isolation after her baby's birth was almost a necessity in that it allowed for a certain mourning over the past. Childhood memories forgotten for years came back quite clearly, from the loneliness of going to school for the first time and times when her parents were angry with her, to happy memories of holidays and times when she'd enjoyed playing alone. Tara felt that much of her depression could be attributed to childlike feelings she was now experiencing in an adult context: strong, bewildering, overwhelming. She found it helpful when she was able to talk to her own mother about her childhood.

More generally, parenthood also means accepting that a certain way of life has passed, at least for now – the time of spontaneity, when you were free to please yourself, get up when you liked, go out to concerts or the cinema when you wanted, and so on. This time may have existed more gloriously in your memory than in fact. The past was also circumscribed, by hours of work, lack of money or energy, perhaps also by the lonely longing for a child. However, once the baby is there it seems as if you're looking back to a fantastic time of unlimited freedom, during which you didn't always make the most of all your opportunities, as found by Antonia.

'Even three years on, I do sometimes still have periods of longing for the past. It feels as though the high point of my life was the two years before I had the baby, when my career was going well. I was travelling, spending a lot of time in America, meeting people, and life was exciting. Even now I sometimes think, maybe I made a mistake, having a baby. But I also realize that there's an element of fantasy in my view of the past – if I'm honest, it wasn't that great. I was lonely, away from my husband a lot, pushing myself, not really that confident. It's just that the change-over is so abrupt – it's from black to white, and the values you have to have for motherhood are so very different from the ones in the outside world. I don't want to give up the experience I've had since the birth. But I'd like to have my cake and eat it, to have a baby and be a bit more free!'

Youth and freedom are two elements much glamourized in our society, while the replacement, motherhood, is not. As Antonia pointed out, this gives plenty of scope for fantasy. One of the snares of depression is false thinking: it is all too easy to be deluded into believing in extremes which don't really exist, or in essentially unrealistic pictures of yourself. This can mix with what Antonia touched on, a sense some women have of actually being a different person since having the baby. Grieving over the past is one thing, and does mellow into acceptance of your new life, but there are also times when you may need to salvage something from the past in order to regain your happiness and sense of direction: contact with a valued old friend who's slipped away in the pressure of your new life; a visit back to a place which used to be important to you. You may even find that when touched directly like this, the past has less meaning than you thought, and that your value for the present is strengthened.

Antonia felt there was no way of bridging the gap between past and present, that having a baby had cut her off completely, that she'd 'gone underground'. Part of her depression was feeling invisible and forgotten by people who had really known her quite well – a feeling of worthlessness. It was only much later that she realized it was possible to write, to phone, to visit and have visitors. She did make a visit back to the United States on a photography trip which, though pleasant, was also stressful. More important than this was the realization that she was revisiting a part of her life which she really had outgrown. The centre of her life had changed more than she had thought, and she cut the trip short to come back because she missed her child.

In need of mothering

The new mother's need for mothering has often been spoken of, but is far from universally met. If a new mother were really to listen to her own needs, she might well opt for more attention than the ritual fortnight after the birth which seems to be the norm before her own mother has to return to the demands of her life. So often too this period means two weeks of family tensions both old and new, as the new mother struggles to prove to her own mother that she is capable. Some older mothers too don't want to intrude; some new mothers just can't accept help. There are plenty of old scripts to be run at this time – that is, behaviour patterns which have hardened into habit, and which you tend to lapse into when with your family. Sometimes these can make for immaturity; equally of course this can be a happy, supportive time which really does draw the family closer together. 'Mothering' of course doesn't have to come from your own mother, it could come from midwives or friends, and is even a certain quality of care which you can try and give yourself. Certainly, a good mothering after the birth lessens the isolation which so many depressed women feel.

However, part of mothering is how well you can accept it. Just as women often expect too much of themselves during their pregnancies, so new mothers often believe they can handle far more than they actually can. Taking on too much can induce a vicious circle of effort and failure which ends with a collapse into depression, often made worse by an impotent kind of anger at yourself. Giving yourself permission not to achieve, lowering your expectations of yourself, can reduce the risk of becoming depressed in this way. It is important not to underestimate the depth of the change motherhood brings. Babies can and do take up all your energy, the more so if you are depressed, and the more you can accept this, the easier it actually is.

> Lucy wanted to get back to lecturing and was very frustrated when she couldn't. It was all she could do to manage the baby: the house was a mess; her memory and concentration were 'shot to pieces' and she simply had no energy for new projects beyond the baby. She had to forget about the whole concept of getting back to normal and to learn to look after herself and the baby first.

Postnatal counsellors frequently warn depressed women not to put pressure on themselves by returning to work before they are ready. This is not true of everyone and some women have been miraculously saved from their depression by going back to work. But work (looked at again in chapter 6) is only one example of how some inner needs can clash with the new mother's even stronger need for mothering. Some depressed women cannot cope with the care of their babies and do need outside help for a while. It is unfortunate that this happens to the more desperate women, giving the 'help' something of a stigma. The help is geared towards supporting the mother until she is able to manage 'on her own' again. That is, independence is the aim – or is it isolation? The idea of long-term help as a normal part of new parenthood, rather than a last resort, seems to have little place in our society. Nevertheless, this is a time to take a pragmatic view of help, not to give lip service to the idea and then struggle on alone, but really to accept whatever help is offered.

Changed relationships— you and your parents

The balance of your relationship with your own parents alters profoundly once you yourself have had a child, and sometimes old conflicts with your parents can underlie postnatal depression. Having a baby is often the final breaking through to the other side, to adulthood, although the period soon after the birth is a time when, no longer just a daughter, you still need looking after. There are times when a parent's help has been substantial.

> Sandra's mother looked after her new baby for seven months until she felt able to cope again. Although Sandra felt guilty and ashamed at

needing so much help, one of the effects was to bring Sandra and her mother closer. Tara described how for many months she would 'take it out on' her mother, who was very patient at these outbursts.

Part of the difficulties of this time can occur if you are looking for ideal mothering. With the extra sensitivity of depression, and having just become a mother yourself, it can sometimes be hard to accept the more humdrum quality usually on offer. But it isn't always the new adults who have problems with their new status: grandparents can be all too human, and it is possible to become depressed if you feel that one of your parents has failed you in some way instead of being supportive when you're in difficulties.

Lucy felt that her mother, Jane, didn't take enough interest in her new granddaughter. Lucy expected her to become more involved as time went on and the baby became more of a person. However, Jane, who'd been widowed some years before, continued to lead her own life.
    'For some reason, she managed almost completely to block the baby out. I suspect it was because it meant I was no longer her little girl. I felt she was quite spiteful in the way she deliberately seemed to withhold support – couldn't she have seen I was in a bad way?'
Later, Lucy felt that the birth of her own baby marked a necessary parting between her mother and herself, a final push into real emotional independence.

It can be hard for some parents to accept that their own children are grown up. Grandchildren, conventionally supposed to be the final fulfilment for an older parent, are also unmistakeable reminders of the passage of time. Some grandparents dislike reminders that they themselves are getting older – not everyone falls gracefully into grandparenthood! This is particularly so if, like Lucy's mother, grandchildren may conjure up memories of a past when her own children were small and her own partner was alive. Another situation is where one of your parents requires a lot of attention from the other.

Jenny's elderly father was the centre of her mother's life. He needed attention more or less constantly as he grew older, and found the noise of very young children increasingly hard to put up with. This naturally made family visits rather tense and Jenny felt threatened at the way her father usurped all her mother's attention, while the baby, as she felt, 'missed out'. Jenny also resented her mother telling her that she spoiled her baby, thinking, 'Why shouldn't I give her a bit of love – *you're* obviously not handing it out.'

This brings up another point, that grandchildren may act as a reminder of a grandparent's past difficulties with her own children, as Tara believed.

'I really think my own mother had postnatal depression. I talked this over with my sister once and we came to the conclusion that this was a distinct possibility. In my memory, she spent her whole time telling us to go away, not always in words. Now, it's sad to say, but I can sometimes feel her fighting the irritation with Bobbie – she just sighs with relief when she can hand him back to me.'

Grandparents as much as parents have all kinds of stereotypes to contend with and may simply find themselves unable to come up to expectations. If you have postnatal depression yourself, it does at least give you a clearer understanding of any difficulties your own mother went through, though hopefully this is only part of a larger, more fulfilling understanding of what it means to be a parent.

When birth triggers past loss

The nature of birth as an experience of loss is shown up sharply when that loss deals with a specific event such as a childhood trauma, relationship difficulties with a parent, or the divorce or death of parents. For Lucy, it was the death of her father in her teenage years.

'I never mourned it – just pushed it away inside. For the rest, I'd never had depression before – I was a very positive person. Birth was a gigantic trigger for me. After the birth, all that grief started coming out, after fourteen years, but I didn't really experience it as a feeling at first. I just felt dead inside, not feeling any emotion except despair. It was only six months later, talking to my therapist, that I was able to cry. I'd been especially close to my father, but my relationship with my mother needed some going over too. My mother worked long hours and I didn't see much of her, and part of my mourning was over what I felt to be her inadequate mothering. I was grieving for what I'd never had from her, for the mother I'd liked to have had, as well as the father I'd lost.'

Mourning like this is a great challenge to any ideals of parenting you are trying to build up. It is an added blow to be thrust right back to a particular situation in childhood or adolescence just when you're faced with the new demands of maturity, to be at once a girl and a mother. (For more on the impact of a parent's death, see *Losing a Parent* by Fiona Marshall (Sheldon Insight 1993).

Mourning, both for particular events and in general, can help bridge that gap, though it is questionable whether you ever fully adapt to being a mother; indeed, why should you? Perhaps you would have to abandon your own individuality entirely for that!

Some element of conflict must remain between your own needs and those of your family; a healthy selfishness and the ability to compromise are perhaps equally as important. However, unsorted conflict can be a large part of depression, in particular the feeling that you've lost sight of yourself in some way. As well as adapting to a new identity as mother, you also need to hold on to an individual, independent self, even if it's only to a minimal extent in the difficult early months or years. Depression can be useful in forcing you to do this – when it hurts that much, you have to change something.

In summing up the whole psychological impact of becoming a mother, Lucy speaks for many women:

'How little it is talked about, and how little you know it's going to turn your life upside down. Everything has to be reassessed – all your relationships, all your expectations.'

This chapter has tried to show how depression plays a part in the adaptation to motherhood which every woman must go through. The positive point about depression from this angle is that it sometimes forces women to change, or to look at their emotions in ways they wouldn't previously have done. The value of this kind of experience, even though it may not be realized during the depression, is of real and lasting importance.

5

Physical Factors

The old saying that it takes nine months to have a baby and another nine to recover physically, takes on new meaning in the context of postnatal depression. Traditionally, postnatal depression has been attributed to a combination of physical causes such as the aftermath of birth and lack of sleep, and environmental factors such as social isolation and the psychological stress of motherhood. Another viewpoint is that an upset in the body's hormonal balance after birth is responsible for postnatal depression.

Many mothers would agree with the view that much depression could be avoided if they could rest more in the first few months. This chapter looks at ways in which physical factors contribute to depression.

It is certainly easy to see how a chain of physical causes can trigger exhaustion and depression: a difficult pregnancy, prolonged labour, a crying newborn, problems with breastfeeding, sleepless nights, to name just a few. Indeed, so obvious do physical factors seem as a cause for depression, that this is probably one reason why women often keep silent about their feelings. They put it all down to broken nights or infected stitches or the drain of breastfeeding, with a conviction that it will pass once the baby is a bit older and more settled, and they've had a chance to get back to a more normal way of living. Perhaps they're justified by the event, because in many cases women do often just 'grow out of' postnatal depression. All too often the statement is heard, 'I only talked about it once it was all over.' However, being convinced it will pass is no reason to do nothing about it; after all, that isn't the way you treat a temporary illness like flu. And, in depression, it isn't always possible to separate mental and physical factors: sometimes physical stress triggers latent mental problems, sometimes your mental attitude prevents you from looking after your physical well-being, and so on.

Pregnancy and postnatal depression

Certainly, your body has had to make massive adaptations in order to produce a baby. *Pregnancy* as well as birth 'takes it out' of you, especially if you've perhaps had a demanding job, or haven't eaten as well as you might have done, or suffered complications such as constant vomiting or even pre-eclampsia. Even when all goes well, the creation of another human being is a marvellously complex process. To take just a few examples of what goes on in pregnancy, your blood volume increases by

48

30 per cent; your uterus ends up 20 times heavier than its pre-pregnancy weight; your heart's workload increases by as much as 40 per cent; your hormonal levels soar, sometimes by as much as 50 times; your ligaments gradually soften in preparation for labour; your breasts become bigger and you gain the average 20–30 lb (9–13.5 kg) weight. The baby absorbs nutrients from your system. During the last weeks, your lungs are squeezed into an ever-smaller space by the growing uterus, making breathing difficult at times.

These are all big changes, which can sometimes make you feel physically wretched. For example, the latter end of pregnancy is notorious for lack of sleep and growing tiredness. Dragging all that extra weight around, feeling breathless if you climb the stairs, perhaps suffering constantly from pain in the ribs (costal margin pain) – it's no wonder if such factors sometimes induce a kind of depression while you're still pregnant. You may long for a delivery which will literally deliver you from such problems, only to find yourself exhausted and tied by babycare.

In this way, you can see how the normal stresses and strains of pregnancy may contribute to depression after the birth. If you've also had some particular complication, like excessive vomiting (*hyperemesis gravidarum*) or pre-eclamptic toxaemia, you may well have felt quite ill and used up. Of course you don't *have* to have depression if you've had a tough pregnancy, but it may be even more important to get more rest after the birth to reduce the risk.

After delivery – physical changes and first visits to doctor

What's also extraordinary is that your body makes many major physical changes back very soon after delivery, within a few days. Nevertheless, it really does take months to recover physically from having a baby. And sometimes postnatal depression may get 'lost' among the immediate after-effects of delivery: swollen breasts, sore bottom, and so on. Feeling awful because of the physical aftermath of the birth (which can last weeks, not days) may be inseparable from depression to such an extent that you may not even realize that you *are* depressed. The six-week check-up can be misleading here. While it is a good time for making sure that you've got over the brunt of the birth, it does rather mark a closing off of the puerperium (period after the birth). After it, there's a tendency to feel that you ought not to have to go back to the doctor for anything connected with the birth; a stitch area that still hurts, for example, or backache. Yet, it is quite common to need further medical attention for months after the birth. As stated in chapter 2, it is possible for a doctor (and yourself) to miss depression at the six-week check-up; similarly, budding physical problems which may contribute to depression may not always receive full attention, perhaps because it is just too early. The six-week checkup is after all to make sure that your body has made its main adjustments after labour (e.g. the uterus returning to the right size). At six weeks, you may not be too bothered about, say, aching stitches or a sore perineum because it's still so soon after the birth. But if four months later your stitch area still hurts and this stops you wanting to make love, your image of yourself and your relationship with your partner may both feel the strain – important factors in depression. Yet, many women feel it's too late to go back to the doctor for this problem, even though it was linked with the birth.

If you are depressed, repeated visits may be seen as a cry for help, your symptoms masking the 'real' cause. It is as ever difficult to see here where mind ends and body begins. After all, if the underlying cause is depression, it doesn't make the headaches any the less real. Or are the recurrent headaches caused by a baby who wakes you constantly at night, and are you in fact 'depressed' because you're simply not being allowed to sleep? Either way, it is still important to consult your GP, even though he or she may not be able to sort the problem out in one go. Repeated visits may be needed to see if you need further help for depression, advice on some aspect of baby management, or further investigation for an underlying health problem. There's more on how the doctor can help in chapter 8.

While on the subject, serious illnesses are much less common than many depressed women expect, who do tend to be frightened that their symptoms indicate that something is really wrong. However, birth can leave you with a whole range of minor physical ailments, which certainly should have attention. Also, constant little illnesses mark the first two years of motherhood for many women; exhaustion, being rundown, make you a prime candidate for the flu that's going round, for the odd tummy bug, and for every spare germ your baby collects from outside groups, too. In this kind of case depression can be linked to 'real' physical illness.

Recovery from birth and babycare – links with depression

Sometimes postnatal depression keeps pace with the general recovery that takes place after pregnancy and birth, though it is perhaps unfortunate to talk about 'recovery' as if having a baby were a major illness instead of being a natural event for a woman. Nevertheless it is important to understand pregnancy and birth make great demands on the body's resources, because some women do start motherhood with these resources somewhat depleted, making them more liable to depression.

So, does it take nine months to recover from a birth? Medically speaking, most of the changes your body needs to make after a pregnancy are complete by then, although some can be delayed if you're breastfeeding. As stated earlier, personal observation from postnatal counsellors has also noted how some mothers' depression does often improve once their baby is around nine months, because they feel better physically. But this can by no means be taken as a hard and fast rule. One piece of research found that a year after birth, half of the women studied still suffered health problems such as backaches and headaches which were related to the birth, and it is easy to see how constant, niggling ill-health of this kind can make you low. There's also the question of how such complaints link with babycare: headaches can be caused by broken nights, backache by carrying round an ever-heavier infant. The exhaustion of birth easily merges into the fatigue of caring for a baby. Indeed, three years has frequently been put forward as a full recovery time, because of the nature of the demands made by very small children.

However, you shouldn't fear that you will actually suffer depression this long. It is more that your priorities undergo a long-term change, and that your energy is directed towards your child instead of activities you previously enjoyed. Letting yourself be totally swamped by the baby, letting the baby rule your life completely, may well contribute to depression. As so much of a small baby's care is physical, you may need to consider ways of making this easier for yourself, as the more rested you are, the less depressed you're likely to feel.

Getting over labour – can it influence depression?

Labour can use your last bit of strength and more. It is not just that the pain is tiring. It is the uncertainty and excitement, culminating in the unbelievable appearance of a baby. It is also mundane matters such as missing a night or two's sleep during the process, as Lucy describes:

'I think the way my labour went certainly paved the way for depression. I missed a night's sleep before the birth because of false alarms and going into hospital to be monitored. Then, after being in labour all night, I missed three more nights' sleep because the baby wanted to suckle the whole time – I couldn't put her down. I was absolutely beside myself by the time I got home from hospital.'

Another danger can be the 'high' which follows a birth (although all some women want to do is sleep!). In the natural excitement after delivery, some women want to stay awake all night talking to their partner, admiring the baby, or perhaps charging up and down the hospital corridors to visit other mums or to ring family and friends with the good news. This is great if you know when to stop. It's when the excitement doesn't wind down, when it takes on a life of its own and propels a new mother into exhaustion, that problems can start. Something snaps and the worn out mother is left as low as previously she was high. From here on, it's a vicious circle of exhaustion and depression which makes some women feel that they pay in months for a few days' or hours' over-excitement after labour. Another feature of excessive post-birth excitement is that it can occasionally be a sign of puerperal psychosis.

You can see then the value of the old-fashioned lying-in period, why hospitals used to insist on bedrest after birth and not too many visitors, the baby taken to the nursery at night and brought to the mother for feeds. All this helps prevent the physical exhaustion which can have such devastating emotional after-effects. Today, however, in many cases women don't give themselves (or aren't given) enough time to get over labour. It isn't just that hospital stays are shorter. It is also that there's less recognition of the need to rest after labour by women themselves as well as by others. It is somehow taken for granted that women will just get on with it when they get home. The idea of a new mother spending days on end in bed is fairly foreign to us, what with the challenge this presents to the housework, to our self-respect, to our whole Puritan heritage of the value of work, cleanliness and being 'busy'.

Suzanne, who came home with her first baby after three days in hospital, 'couldn't rest'. Finding the house in a mess after her absence, she wasn't happy until she'd thoroughly cleaned it, and after that there was always some other little job to do. The strain of this increased her lochia (blood flow after delivery) to an alarming extent. When the visiting midwife found out what she'd been doing, she was horrified, and banished Suzanne to bed!

Difficult as it may be to ignore the begging chores, you have to take note of your own need for rest. Shocking though the thought may be, days in bed may be exactly what you need now, and the inconvenience caused is probably greater in your head than in reality. Indeed (to continue along Puritan lines) time out, letting go, is a *duty* you owe to yourself and your family. Rest now, after the birth, may help prevent overtiredness and depression later on. Selfishness now may make you a better mother in the long run.

Caesarean birth

Birth by caesarean section now accounts for around one in nine deliveries. A caesarean is major surgery and needs more recovery time – six weeks to get over the main effects of the operation, but maybe as much as six months before your energy really starts coming back. Drugs used during the operation may result in depression for a few days afterwards; you may also be traumatized by the reason why you had to have the caesarean, if you nearly did lose the baby or were in danger yourself. If you had a long, difficult labour before the caesarean was decided on, you may already have been exhausted by the time you reached the operating table. Again, caesareans are sometimes done if the placenta breaks away from the uterus (*abruptio placenta*) in which case the mother may lose blood and so end up feeling weak and even in need of a transfusion. As you can see, there are many reasons why this operation may leave you feeling especially weak and so perhaps more prone to depression. Carrie hated the post-op helplessness:

'I had a general anaesthetic and when I woke up I was desperately thirsty and only allowed sips of water. I was so groggy I was afraid I'd drop the baby. I had needles in both hands, one for a drip and one for a transfusion – a nurse had to give me the baby the first day. Once the transfusion was over, if I wanted to go to the loo I had to push the drip in front of me – this huge hat-stand thing with a bag of saline or whatever on it. The first time I got up I thought I was going to fall apart in the middle – the wound really did hurt. I felt so vulnerable. I kept shaking – the after-effects of the drug, I think. When our old family doctor dropped by to see me, I disgraced myself by bursting into tears.'

It may seem obvious that caesareans need more care afterwards, but in practice this is often ignored because of the variety of pressures to which a woman may feel subject.

Carrie came home from hospital a week after her caesarean; the next day, she felt obliged to get out of bed and cook for her mother-in-law, who was visiting. She also had a stream of visitors for whom she felt obliged to make tea, when she was really still too exhausted even to get out of bed.

Given the way Carrie felt after her caesarean, it is hardly surprising that she did succumb to depression.

Do make other people understand that you have just been through a major operation and that they must do the tea-making! You may also need to keep a lookout for other physical factors which can pull you down after a caesarean: an infected wound (inflammation or pus) and anaemia are two possibilities. Mobility is important after this operation to prevent thrombosis; while still in hospital, you'll be given exercises to do – try and keep them up at home, too. Your milk and lochia will come in as normal – so may the baby blues.

Once home, you may be dismayed at how soggy your tummy still looks. This is because the surgeon has to cut through several layers to reach the womb. You should make sure you follow the dictates to do less physically, so you don't further strain these tummy muscles; no heavy lifting for the first six weeks to save your tummy muscles. Remember too that you will tire more quickly. Even if a caesarean may seem to make you a prime candidate for postnatal depression, the worst of the physical effects can be warded off with care. So look after yourself, eating and resting properly, and do accept *all* offers of help.

Twin birth

Again, a twin birth may make you more predisposed to depression if you allow yourself to become or remain too physically exhausted. Some mothers who have had twins have reported being too washed out even to stand without help the first day or so after the birth. And of course many twins are delivered by caesarean anyway. In addition, twin pregnancy makes extra demands on the body, so that some of the side-effects of pregnancy will be felt more, such as weight gain; you also have two babies taking the nutrients they need from you. As with a caesarean, proper diet, self-care, rest and help can all stave off depression.

After-effects of drugs in labour

Drugs affect people in different ways: some love gas and air, a few swear by pethidine, and some women refuse to go through labour without an epidural. Others, however, can't find a type of pain relief that suits them and find that the pain may be dulled, but that they end up with an awful hangover to add to their other post-labour miseries!

One feature of drugs during birth – not always recognized – is that the immediate effects can linger on for as much as a week or two after the birth, perhaps causing dopiness, irritability and vivid bad dreams. Headache and backache have also been linked with epidurals.

The hormone story

One theory which remains controversial but important is that hormonal changes after birth are responsible for postnatal depression. Because of the delicate biochemical links between mind and body, these changes are thought to affect the brain and cause such symptoms as sleeping or eating disturbances, crying, confusion and extreme irritability.

Hormones are tiny but powerful substances which are complex and far-reaching in their effects on the body. Their normal functions are wide and include control of all the body's activities, such as growth, temperature control and digestion. It is certainly beyond question that too much or too little of some hormones can affect the body. For example, dwarfism is attributed to a shortage of growth hormone in the pituitary gland; while overactivity in the thyroid gland, which produces a hormone controlling the body's metabolic rate, can result in weight loss, rapid heartbeat and extreme feelings of nervousness. In fact, women with postnatal depression are occasionally tested for underactivity of the thyroid.

In pregnancy, normal hormone levels soar, sometimes by as much as 30 to 50 times the normal rate, while the body also produces special hormones which aren't found in the body at any other time. Changes in hormonal levels account for all sorts of side-effects in pregnancy, such as morning sickness, breast swelling and even the need to urinate more often, especially at night.

The two major hormones involved in making a baby are progesterone and oestrogen. Both play vital roles in the body even before conception. Oestrogen helps develop sexual characteristics such as the breasts and vulva; progesterone helps regulate the menstrual cycle. It is the levels of these hormones which increase so greatly during pregnancy, often resulting in the traditional pregnancy 'bloom' and feelings of well-being. Other hormones include prolactin, which helps prepare the breasts for the production of milk after the birth.

With the delivery of the baby, the hormones, which have been building up to such high levels for months, drop abruptly. Within hours, they are found only in minute amounts, with the exception of prolactin, large amounts of which are needed for the production of breastmilk. The special hormones which appear to be produced only during pregnancy disappear completely.

It is these great drops in hormone levels which are thought by some to be the trigger to depression in some women, quite apart from the stress of birth. Women who experience the greatest drop in progesterone have been shown to be more prone to depression. There is also some evidence to show that women who are particularly vulnerable seem to be those who have felt better than average during pregnancy, with positive attitudes which could be partly attributable to high amounts of progesterone in their system. There is more on hormone treatment for postnatal depression in chapter 8.

You and your body

To sum up, it can be seen that birth can provoke a wide range of physical reactions which can easily result in feelings of exhaustion or even illness. Some women believe their depression was indeed caused by a combination of physical factors; others feel that physical causes plus other factors such as a stretched partnership or a crying baby tipped them 'over the edge'.

A final point to be considered is your own body image. Just after giving birth, you probably feel hugely relieved – yet it can be a shock to look into a mirror, as Antonia found.

'When the baby came out, I remember thinking, at last, at last! I'd felt so heavy and cumbersome. I couldn't believe the size of the placenta either – huge. No wonder I'd felt so weighed down. When I got home the next day the first thing I did was to jump on the scales. I almost wept with disappointment – I was still a stone overweight. My tummy was flabby and ghastly, like some bloated old woman, my face was desperate, as if I'd been in a fight or had a bad hangover, I looked so shattered. I felt I was looking at a stranger.'

This feeling of disappointment or even alienation usually passes: excess weight is lost in the week or so after delivery in the form of fluid, the tummy muscles gradually recover in the weeks following, and so on. Sometimes, though, a poor body image can be very much bound up with depression. This may be specifically related to becoming a mother: some women now feel that it's all over and they're 'just a mum', a mum being a drab and overweight being with no time to spare for her own appearance. Others feel overwhelmed by the messiness of babies, who posset (bring up milk) and later spread food over their clean clothes. Yet others feel they've lost all desirability as women, that their mystique has gone for their partner, especially if he was present at the birth. Whereas a pregnant body had a beauty and form of its own, a body which has just given birth can be experienced as empty now that the baby has gone, yet still retaining those useless extra folds of fat, the stretchmarks.

It does take time for your body to get over the birth, but it's amazing what it's capable of. Remember too that excess fat is purposely retained by nature for breastfeeding; perhaps too to cushion the mother who often finds the weight just falls off as she runs round after her baby all day! You certainly should not diet after a birth, and this and other tips will be looked at in more detail in chapter 9.

More important than how much you weigh or how you look is feeling comfortable with the physical self who has emerged from the birth. Treat yourself as gently as possible; remember that your body has just produced another human being. As such it is entitled both to respect and to time in which to recover from such an amazing achievement.

6

Social Factors

Mothers suffer from a notorious lack of social identity – that is, motherhood usually brings none of the big rewards with which society rewards those who are deemed to have 'achieved': huge wages, titles, status, taxis, seats at the opera, private medicine, company cars, annual bonuses, publicity, gasps of respect or awe. It's a low-key job, done strictly behind the scenes. Outsiders may not be quite sure exactly what a mother does, and (unlike the private life of a celebrity such as Madonna) they certainly aren't going to waste too much energy finding out. In our society mothers are invisible, or at least faceless, beings who propel a pushchair down an indifferent street, noticed only when they quarrel with their tiny children at supermarket tills.

At the same time, mothers are victims of insistent social myths. The first is that their commitment to their children not only comes before all else, but rules out all other interests and passions. This myth that a mother is an utterly devoted being means they can be sentimentalized as the very backbone of the society which ignores them. Mother and baby, mother and home, mother at the stove, mother at Christmas – the images are propagated endlessly in the world of advertising, both mirroring and dictating how we think. Consider what the word 'mother' means to you – it's difficult to consider its meaning without being swamped by a hundred uncalled-for clichés. Society's images of 'mother' can make it difficult to feel that you, a mother, are an individual. Feelings of being socially insignificant can merge with those of the isolation which can be so strong in depression. But this depression and isolation can form an area within which it is possible to carve out a stronger individual identity than you've ever had before. In other words, being stuck with yourself, alone and miserable, means that you can begin to learn more about yourself, perhaps for the first time – to rely on yourself more, to like yourself more.

Of course, no one is an island, and there is no point sitting miserably alone at home because you think it is character-forming. This kind of new strength is more an end product of depression, and, while building it up, you may need more outside help, not less. This is where other mothers who've been through depression can be so helpful. The point is, if all mothers are socially insignificant, they form a social sub-group which then acquires a status of its own, along with the possibility of action and power. To take it at its simplest, meeting just one mother whom you feel you can talk to can alter your whole social (even your world) view. Putting it more widely, it is mothers who run the Association for Postnatal Depression, which has done so much to raise awareness of postnatal depression and give comfort to other depressed women. In other words, you don't have to be swamped by society's attitude to motherhood, even in depression: two mothers talking honestly together form a society of their own.

Many women do find that their own more valid experience of motherhood has to be carved out in the privacy of their own homes. In the end, what other experience other than the private really counts? We are social beings, but we each experience motherhood in a unique, individual way. It can be worth differentiating between your own private experience of motherhood (complex, contradictory, ambivalent?) and what you understand to be society's view of motherhood (simplistic, dictatorial?). Indeed, the gap between the two can be a great part of depression for some women. 'You never see babies being sick on TV.' 'The adverts just show a soft-focus mother with a dear little freshly-washed baby – not an old hag in a sweaty nightgown struggling to breastfeed.'

The feeling of isolation can, as just mentioned, be a major part of depression (something which can in fact colour your perception of outside social factors). You may actually be more isolated than usual, if, for example, you're now at home with a baby after having been at work. The pregnant woman does have a fair amount of recognition from the social machine, with regular visits to ante-natal clinics and so on. In fact, after the build-up of pregnancy, the mother can feel socially stranded just at the time when she has to build up a new individual identity. Perhaps, then, in retrospect, a period of depression can be seen as a prelude to a new way of being with people, almost a necessary period of solitude before your new social and private selves merge to meet others on a deeper, more understanding level. This chapter looks at how depression and social factors interrelate.

So, what exactly are the 'social factors' sometimes said to cause or contribute to postnatal depression? Obvious social disadvantages such as poverty and poor housing have been blamed, but this certainly doesn't exempt the rich and well-housed from the condition. It is also been suggested that socially disadvantaged people should form one of the sub-groups into which postnatal depression should be divided, because of the different pressures they may experience. Apart from the fact that depression does cut across all society, this would be difficult to do in a society already so roughly reshaped by recession. Nevertheless, some women have described how their depression improved once a housing problem was sorted out, or once their unemployed partner managed to get a job.

Lucy thought her depression was increased by the flat they were living in: every time the person upstairs used the washing machine, it leaked through into their kitchen; the view was depressing; and she longed for a garden for her baby. The family's move away from the town centre to a house in the suburbs certainly coincided with the lifting of her depression. 'From the day we moved in to the new house, I started feeling so much better.'

Unfortunately, a move isn't always possible – nor does it always automatically make for increased happiness. Unsorted problems have a way of moving house with you. Even so, there is no doubt that where and how you live radically affects your concept of yourself. The degree of comfort and style you need in order to maintain your dignity does vary from person to person, and to fall below this comfortable level can certainly contribute to depression. With motherhood, however – especially new motherhood – this can sometimes be difficult to assess. The conditions of life are changed anyway by having a baby to care for. You may have a house and lifestyle which lack nothing, only to find life a torment because of a baby who won't stop crying.

Concepts of motherhood

There are certain cultural expectations of motherhood which reach everyone no matter what her social status. These start to be thrown into relief if you consider the mores of other countries. For example, in Scandinavia it has been fashionable for parents to go backpacking with a baby or toddler, taking a young child on more adventurous, open-air holidays than are usual in this country. In certain parts of Africa a six-week period of rest and segregation for a mother after birth is normal. Both customs imply different kinds of freedom for mothers; one, the freedom to roam, the other, the freedom to rest. Here, perhaps the most damaging concept of motherhood is the one which sees the mother as unselfish, devoted, certainly not requiring pay or other vulgar material manifestations of social esteem (apart, perhaps, at Mother's Day).

The myth of the selfless mother is less than helpful to the woman suffering from postnatal depression, whose personal needs may be urgent. To say this is by no means to imply that she's too taken up with her own troubles to care for her baby. You can still be a good mother even if you are depressed, or, more simply, even if you have needs of your own. But to some extent, the cultural expectations of selflessness are reinforced by the nature of babycare, when you do often have to put your needs on hold. At some point in your depression, though, you will probably have to put yourself first. You have to find your own way out of the myth that mother and baby are all in all to each other, excluding everyone else. This may involve being selfish about some aspect of babycare which is proving just too much, whether it's demand breast-feeding at eight months, or the constant getting up at night. After all, it isn't going to harm your baby if you gently start to wean her, or to try and teach her to sleep through the night.

'Postnatal illness' –
a modern Western disease?

Our own society has had different views of postnatal depression. In the Middle Ages, a woman suffering from depression was likely to have been seen either as a witch or under a witch's curse, and treated accordingly; later, postnatal depression fell under the perhaps equally potent curse of silence. In other societies in modern times, different explanations have been put forward for postnatal disorders: in Africa for example, causes cited have included the mother's promiscuity during pregnancy and excessive body heat, with symptoms of cannibalistic feelings towards the baby, restlessness and confusion. In other words, different societies have their own ways of acknowledging that having a baby is a major life event which can trigger different reactions. Indeed, one explanation of postnatal depression in our society is that this achievement is recognized up to delivery and immediate postnatal care, but that there is no continuing social recognition of the mother's achievement.

Is there something in our society which makes mothers more vulnerable to depression? Is it industrialization, urbanization, the loss of the village community and the extended family, the medicalization of birth, role confusion in women, and so on? Before you leap up with an avid 'Yes!' consider the alternative of giving birth in a small society where everyone, with all his or her limitations, is wearyingly familiar; where you are so used to the view of unbroken fields that you hardly notice them; where life is dictated by what time the sun rises and sets and follows the same routine day in and day out. Birth is still painful, and presided over by the local midwife who is so wrapped up in traditional views of childbirth that she doesn't listen to what you say. When the baby is born, your mother, grandmother and aunts all have their own strong views on how it should be brought up, so that any little stirrings of independent thought you have are soon quashed. In other words, living in a small, rural, tightknit society should not be romanticized. We do sometimes tend to have a vision of a rural golden age where men and women were more in touch with nature, but simply going back in time may not be the answer. For example, used as we have become to privacy, could we now cope with the constrictions imposed by the extended family?

Research into traditional societies in other cultures doesn't always find what we call postnatal depression, and family and social structures are often much tighter and more supportive, especially in the first six weeks after the birth. For example, in Jamaica, there has been a traditional period of segregation where a mother stays at home and is looked after by her own mother for the first six weeks. In China, extra attention is given to the mother by her family and social contacts. In our own society, the six-week postnatal check-up has been seen a similar ritual, marking the end of the special period after the birth. Christening or other naming rituals may also take place around this time. What does seem to be lacking is the interim period of continuous social support.

Work

'I didn't really get over my depression until I went back to work.' This is a comment made fairly often in relation to postnatal depression. Does it then imply that the best and quickest cure for postnatal depression is to speed back to work? That it really is 'all in the mind' and that a good healthy dose of work will 'take you out of yourself'?

There are mothers who feel they can't face going back to work because of their depression, and counsellors who advise them not to take on more than they can handle, certainly not to rush the return to work. But it may not be as simple as just staying home because you haven't the energy for work. Attitudes to work are one of the things which change most profoundly – and unpredictably – with motherhood. The unsuspected physical fatigue of baby-rearing may well make the return to work a daunting prospect, though there are also the mothers who 'go to work for a rest'! However, when it comes to the point, many women find they don't want to leave the baby, and the conflict this causes between your old and new attitude can contribute to depression. It can be hard to accept that you and your priorities have changed, especially if there is also some financial pressure to take up work again. Even those who do choose to go back may experience grief at this separation.

Carrie, a systems analyst, spent most of the weekend weeping before her return to work on the Monday. She knew however that staying at home with a baby was emphatically not for her. Her depression was helped by going back to work, and she felt it would have got worse had she stayed at home. Even so, she felt the pain of separation from her baby 'almost physically' at first.

It is worth being careful about going back to work if you are suffering from postnatal depression. For some women, it enhances their identity greatly to know that they are visible again, have a stronger social identity and are earning money, and all this can be quite enough to cure the depression. But for others, going back can create more pressures than it resolves. The demands of trying to combine motherhood and work can take their toll in terms of stress and health anyway, the more so if you are depressed and/or physically rundown after a birth and months of sleepless nights. If in doubt, give work a try, but keep an open mind and don't put too much pressure on yourself to continue. If you need the money, you may feel you don't have much choice but to return to work even if you may not really feel ready to. Talk it over carefully with someone you trust, your partner and/or your doctor perhaps. How strong do you really feel? Who or what is pressurizing you to return to work? Are there economies you could make which would relieve you of the need to work for the time being? Is part of your depression because you're deeply longing to stay with the baby? In this day and age, it is difficult voluntarily to let go of work when so many people are clinging hard to their jobs, and this kind of social pressure can make the traditional work/motherhood decision even harder. (For more on combining work and motherhood, you might like to look at *Managing Two Careers* by Patricia O'Brien, Sheldon Press 1989.)

Staying at home after working

If you've been used to going out to work, staying at home with a small baby can seem very strange, with no deadlines, no feedback, no external rewards. Even the busiest job has a cut-off point, even if that's only sleep, and you can always snatch five minutes to make a coffee. Lucy had particular difficulties in adjusting to being at home after working.

After a busy job as a lecturer and teacher, Lucy found the lack of structure and visible achievement as a mother frustrating.
'Even though I wasn't working I was doing too much – busy busy busy! Talk about high expectations and superwoman! I had this awful sense of guilt from my religious background, the feeling that I had to be seen to be doing something – yet the baby never let me finish anything. In the end it all got too much and I sort of collapsed mentally and suddenly I couldn't even cope with basic housework. I'd been doing nothing and I'd be absolutely exhausted, my head spinning.'
In the end, Lucy realized she could not be a completely full-time mother even though she did not want to return to full-time work either. She took on ten hours of private coaching a week – enough to give structure to her days.

This sort of decision may not be possible in mid-depression – you may need help from family, friends or a support organization before you reach this point. However, without putting pressure on yourself, it may be worth asking yourself whether the stimulus of work would be of help in beating the depression, if not for now, then for the future. It may not be possible to continue your old career, nor may you want to. With the changes motherhood and depression can bring, some women change course after having a baby, arranging a job or a new business around the family rather than vice versa. Even in the depths of your depression, you can ask yourself what undeveloped talents you may have which could be put to future use: for cooking and catering? for arts and crafts? for listening? Bowing out of the pressure of an old job may eventually mean that you find a new, more flexible career.

Changed relationships with friends

Friends are a very important part of your social structure; you may not realize how important until that structure is changed by a baby, and perhaps by the depression that can come with a baby. Many friendships do undergo changes after a birth, changes which often mirror the deep personal adaptation you make as you grow into motherhood. Over the months, there is a natural process after a birth whereby you may find that some friendships are suspended temporarily, some left behind altogether, some strengthened, some new ones gaining importance. In fact, having a baby can be quite a test of friendship, especially if you feel you've had difficulties which your peers haven't.

Your friends may not understand if you talk about your postnatal depression; other women who've had babies may be puzzled by your feelings, perhaps unresponsive or preoccupied with their own problems. It may be better for a while to make an effort to get in touch with other women who have been through a similar experience. The 'Useful addresses' section at the back of this book gives suggestions on where to find people who can offer both support and understanding.

Generally, it is quite common to see far less of people in the first year or so after a birth, because babycare simply absorbs all your energy – the more so if you are depressed. This change in your social pattern can in itself be quite upsetting, because it is yet another of those aspects of parenthood which no one warns you of in advance, and where you think you are the only person on earth suffering!

Jenny and her husband had always given lots of dinner parties and a good social life was important to them. They both felt that life was constricted and dull after the baby's birth, when Jenny was often too tired to cook or even to talk to guests. When people did come, the baby absorbed much of Jenny's attention and she often felt she had to go upstairs to breastfeed. Jenny began to feel cut off and her social confidence was undermined, especially as she felt that people weren't returning invitations because the baby was seen as too much of a problem.

It may well have been that Jenny was signalling, explicitly or not, that social life with a baby was just too much. You may well have said much the same yourself: 'We don't go out so much now', or, 'We find it so hard to get out with the baby', and so on. As a result, people are hesitant to offer invitations which may be felt as a strain on the guest, although you may be more sensitive to 'rejection' if you're depressed. But it *is* more difficult to see other friends and look after a small baby; this is a time of changing priorities in which your previous social life does naturally undergo modifications.

However, it is possible to attend to a baby and to guests as well, to give the baby a discreet breastfeed or a cuddle while carrying on a conversation, so long as you have the energy to face other people. It is this that may be missing if you are depressed, as Tara describes:

'I think I was sheltering behind the baby – whenever people came round I'd be in the kitchen or looking after the baby. It just seemed like too much effort to talk to them; they didn't have anything to say that I wanted to hear, and I know I had nothing to say in return!'

Depression can certainly show up the superficiality of some friendships; you may suddenly realize that you just can't have the sort of talk you're longing to have with any of the people you know. You may also have a share of 'fair-weather friends' or, to put it more sympathetically, people who don't feel able to cope with the depression they sense in you. Don't worry though if you do feel you have nothing to say – it will all come out once you find the right listener. You may need to talk at some length about deep personal feelings before you can take a renewed interest in current issues, culture and gossip.

Peer pressure

Your relationship with your baby is now central, so that everyone else has to settle down around this. But some women do feel under pressure to prove themselves to their former friends and work colleagues, to prove that they haven't changed and can still compete on the old levels. At the same time, depression may make you more vulnerable and 'clingy' than usual. You may want to seek reassurance from long-term friends, to cling to former sources of emotional security, even, sometimes, to refuse to admit that relationships have changed.

> Sandra tried to meet her nursing colleagues for a drink in the pub every so often after the birth, but found she was out of the swing of it and no longer interested in hospital gossip. She would end up sitting silent in a corner, feeling very depressed and longing to go home to bed.
>
> Lucy found that a gulf had opened up between herself and her previous work friends, who were fairly committed to a high-pressure, childless life. She spent much mental energy worrying about how they perceived her and her growing depression, and even more energy trying to keep in touch with them on their terms, for example meeting them outside for lunch when it was really too much trouble for her, instead of getting them to pop round to the house. She felt her colleagues disapproved of her having a baby because it interrupted her career, especially as one of two of them greeted her birth announcement card with 'It hasn't made me change my mind!'

While you might normally be able to laugh off the defiance of the childless, you may well overreact to insensitive comments because of depression. Friends without children can be especially valuable later on, contrasting with and enriching your own family life. For now, they may very well not realize the kind of pressures you are under. Struggling to meet a friend for lunch or a drink with a late babysitter or a baby who refuses to go into a sling, while your friend only has to skip out of her office, may be more trouble than it's worth. On the other hand, you may feel the meeting will get you out of the depression for a while. Do try and make it easy on yourself; see the people who make you feel good, not those who leave you feeling undermined. If you're going out, start your preparations earlier. Have the confidence to ask others to accept your changed circumstances – get them to come round to the house and perhaps bring part of a lunch with them. And remember, any friendship worth its salt will endure a few months' upheaval or neglect until you get over your depression.

Mothers with mothers – comparing

What about old friends who have had babies, or new ones made at antenatal classes or the hospital? Surely having motherhood in common can cut across depression? This is true if you are fortunate enough to meet someone who is on your wavelength, and brave enough to voice your real feelings. Often, however, women find themselves as if sworn to silence – they can't break through with the truth no matter how much they want to. It is easy to underestimate the pressure which mothers feel to appear to be coping, not to be the only person in the group of new mothers who can't breastfeed, or who gets angry with her baby. The word 'depression' is not exactly taboo, but it does need the building up of a sensitive and confidential friendship between mothers before it can be mentioned. This isn't to say that problems aren't discussed, but they may be done so only in the tone set by the group; one of tolerant exasperation, perhaps, or of humour. Mothers who aren't depressed will usually be ready to let their problems go once they've 'let off steam', and talk about something else; mothers who are depressed may need to talk a lot longer than others can comprehend, seeking sometimes obsessively for the perfect solution.

There is a natural tendency to compare your performance as a mother with that of others. There is the delicate balance between the secret knowledge that your own child is the best, and the fear that everyone else is making a better job of parenthood than you! In times of depression, with the vast threat posed to your own identity and ability to cope, this balance is much easier to lose. How others manage can seem at once an important example to be followed at all costs, and as remote as if it were in another world. One reason why some depressed women won't see other people is this hopeless conviction that these others live in another universe, one far too competent and happy for contact to be other than damaging to the one who's low. Such reminders of happiness can only bring pain. For those who can bring themselves to mingle, the competitive relationships between mothers can be almost as close, as intricate and as obsessive as between lovers, as Antonia describes.

'One of the most maddening parts of my experience was trying to talk to this other mother, whom I saw quite a lot of because she lived nearby. No matter what I tried to tell her about my feelings, she always got in first. No matter what I felt, she'd been there before, felt it too, only worse. She had a complete monopoly on all bad feelings. Yet she quite obviously wasn't depressed, as I was – she was out and about with all sorts of people, whereas she was about the only person I ever saw. Her house was always immaculate, very unlike mine. And I know it sounds mean and envious, but she had more money to spend than me, too, and was always buying bits for the baby's room, you know, the very items which I'd have loved but could never have afforded. In the end, I used to feel that our whole relationship was based on envy, that she would deliberately go out and buy what I wanted, in order to make herself feel good and me bad.'

One of the most distressing aspects of depression is the deep lack of confidence it entails, something which certainly played a part in Antonia's relationship with her friend. This kind of competitiveness can sometimes lead to compulsive spending as women try to buy their child exactly what other children have. This can sometimes result in bad feeling with a partner if he feels you are spending too much or being taken in by others' values. As far as Antonia was concerned, she found that her envy gradually decreased as her own confidence grew, until finally she was able completely to reassess this situation.

'I realized that our priorities were in fact different – whereas I did quite like the idea of a stylish, tasteful house, I wasn't willing to put it as one of my firsts, which she did – she was always hoovering and tidying; the child was barely allowed to have its toys out. I realized that I preferred to spend money on books for my baby than on ornaments for his room. In fact, I later thought that she was quite an insecure person, maybe someone who needed to spend a lot of money in order to boost her self-image.'

A greater flexibility in how she regarded people was one good result of Antonia's relationship, a new willingness to suspend judgement, not to take others at face value, and a stronger confidence in her own identity and abilities as a person and as a parent.

One aspect of the depression which may not even be recognized, let alone controlled, is denigration of yourself or your child. It is painful to hear a mother running her own child down (and by implication herself), but sometimes not so easy to hear yourself doing the same, or to hear the plea for reassurance behind negative words.

Tara's partner Al used to tell her off for the way she spoke about baby Bobbie – he was 'clumsy', 'always last', or 'too podgy'. There was more than one row as Tara just couldn't understand what he was going on about. In the end, Al got a close friend to have a word with her. Tara admitted she didn't want her little boy to turn out 'like me' – she felt her own mother hadn't made that wonderful a job of bringing her up, and wanted to do better herself.

Tara's words show how some women enter into unconscious competition with their own mothers, perhaps living out feelings from their own girlhoods of being rejected or thought not good enough. Recognizing the unconscious patterns which can dominate a life is where a trained counsellor can be so useful, although you may find it enough to talk matters over with a partner or friend. The important thing is being willing to recognize your own patterns, and being willing to try and change them.

Beating isolation

This section on friendship has been relatively long because of the isolation and lack of self-worth so many depressed women feel. Warm, supportive friends are more necessary than ever when you're brought low in this way, and it doesn't always take that much to lift your spirits; sometimes a quick meeting can act like a magic pill, even if the effect is temporary.

> Carrie noticed how a coffee with a friend would banish her depression and keep it off for a few hours. Marcia would be shaken from the depths of gloom by a phone call and manage to enjoy the chat, even though it didn't lift her spirits for long afterwards.

When you're deeply depressed, social contact may be beyond you. In this case, don't worry about it: it may even be that the depression knows what is best for you, and is protecting you against the strain of too much contact with people. What you certainly don't need are people who exhaust you or who make you feel bad about yourself in any way, who criticize your handling of the baby or who are keen to find solutions to your problems but not to listen to you talk.

If you feel that you're really isolated within yourself, and that the depression is severe rather than protective; if you find yourself thinking of suicide, you must take steps to talk to someone. It isn't melodramatic to call the Samaritans or any other supportive organization – that is what they are there for – just five minutes chat may be enough. Even just dialling the phone number may help.

Better still, try not to let yourself become that isolated. Keep the social lines open: talk on the phone if you can't meet; if you can't manage to get out, invite people round. Tidy one room if the house is a mess and shut the other doors. Or even ask your friend to help you get straight; now may be a time for receiving in friendship, rather than giving. And if this bothers you, don't worry. Once you have recovered, there will still be women who may need just what you can give. You may even have more to give just because like them you've been through this hard experience and have known what it's like to lose for a while that feeling of equality which makes the best of friendships so enriching.

7

Fathers and Postnatal Depression

Much of the emphasis as regards postnatal depression has been on the suffering of women. But, while fatherhood is achieving more social recognition, it can sometimes be overlooked that men also have to go through the adjustment to parenthood. This chapter looks at how men may become depressed as they adapt to fatherhood. It also examines the changes relationships undergo as partners become parents, and the effect of depression on a relationship. The last section of the chapter contains advice on what to do if you know someone who is suffering from postnatal depression, and is written for parents and friends of the woman as well as for a partner.

Men may suffer a kind of depression of their own after the birth, or they can suffer indirectly by having to bear with the changed behaviour of their partner. Either way, they too have to cope with the gap between previous fantasies of parenthood and the reality, and may be worse off than women in two particular respects: men's ideas of parenting may be less defined, and they may have even less social support than women.

If women have little contact with babies before their own are born, men have even less. One result can be that fatherhood becomes an impersonal macho myth, with almost ritualized ideas of children. 'A son to play football with/inherit the family name', 'a daughter to love me in old age', are not outworn concepts, even if they're not precisely admitted in conscious thought. This kind of thinking in outline leaves men quite unprepared for the real details of one small, noisy baby.

Men can also suffer more than women in having less of a social network. After all, however depressed a woman may be, she does have some recognition of postnatal depression in the outside world, as well as several support groups. It's also more acceptable for women to talk about their emotions, especially their emotions as parents. It is not as common for two or three fathers to get together and talk about fatherhood as women do about motherhood. However, concepts of fatherhood are changing, and men do have some outlets if they need to talk about their emotions. There are many more support groups for parents today, which meet regularly and run courses; some of these have emphasized the acceptability of tears (big boys can cry) as a vehicle for men's emotions. For some men, office chitchat is just as likely to be about parenthood as about sport; there are more articles and books about fatherhood. The dangers with fatherhood becoming mildly 'trendy' are that it can perpetuate a myth of another kind: the sentimental strong father, for example, or the flawed post-new man who marvels and understands when his baby cries, tells his mates about it but hasn't quite got to grips with nappy changing! Thus the complex underlying issues can be glossed over with a kind of self-conscious humour; one kind of group acceptability is replaced by another.

Another outlet for men can be their own fathers, who may provide unexpected empathy with their sons' emotions, and pride at becoming a grandfather. It is natural that men re-examine their relations with their fathers on having their own baby, and some do find that they are a better source of support than might have been thought. Finally, of course, men also have their partners to talk to about their feelings; indeed, sadly, some women's depression can be increased by feeling that they have to support their partners as well as everything else. But, as far as the partnership is concerned, it is perhaps better that the lines of communication are kept open even if it is only him grumbling yet again! Being truthful about discontents and needs may be painful and tiring when the woman is absorbed in her own depression, but a creeping lack of communication after the baby is born is one major factor in creating discontent in a relationship.

How her postnatal depression may affect a relationship

A baby traditionally changes a couple's relationship and psychologists have found many links between postnatal depression and an unsatisfying relationship between partners. The romantic view is that a baby 'brings you closer together'. But realistically, the stresses of babycare, and postnatal depression in particular, can show up all the old cracks in a relationship, and plenty of new ones too. Indeed, research has indicated that the first five years of a child's life are in some ways the hardest as partners struggle with major adaptations – emotional, economic, social. If the woman is very depressed, such adaptations are obviously going to be much harder.

One classic reaction to parenthood is for partners to fall back into roles because it is simply the easiest way to manage: he goes out to work, she undertakes baby-rearing at home. The unexpectedness of finding yourself thrust back into these traditional patterns can make modern expectations of equal partnerships look very naïve. A particular bone of contention for women is babycare; if the woman is depressed and not coping with this very well, it's easy for her to feel that the man just isn't doing his share. Social work structures do certainly make it difficult for the man to share babycare as much as he might because the man, out at work all day, simply isn't there to change the nappies and get to know the baby.

If as well as this the man wants some emotional support, the depressed woman can feel unbearably pressurized. It may be no more than the man needing to talk about a bad day at work, or it may be that there are real financial difficulties which need serious discussion. Whereas before the birth the woman may have taken routine grousings or money discussion in her stride, now they can seem like one more emotional strain dragging her down, as Lucy describes:

'Roger was going through rather a bad patch himself and I'm afraid my heart used to sink when I heard his key in the lock. In one way I'd be dying for him to come home and help – some adult company – but the reality was he'd come in with that long face yet again and just collapse with a drink and the TV. Then I'd have to hear it all again – how he thought he was being passed over for promotion, not appreciated enough, heading for redundancy, etc. I used to feel the most terrible insecurity – terror, really. I felt he was wilfully making things worse by being so negative. Then when I showed impatience he'd accuse me of being selfish. It was a terrible vicious circle, and we had terrible rows. Both of us were needing more support than we got from each other.'

A baby alters the balance of the couple's previous relationship, and it can be hard accepting that you don't have as much time for each other as before. In particular, a birth dispels to some extent any parenting that went on between the man and the woman before the birth. Perhaps she babied him, or perhaps he protected her from the big bad world. When these aspects of a relationship fade away under the impact of the baby, feelings of sadness and loss can be created on both sides. Another factor in depression is any differences between partners about how much the baby was really wanted; the classic example is the woman wanting the baby more than the man, but the reverse can also be true.

It is important to deal with dissatisfactions early, not to let them be shelved by the depression or by the baby; indeed, depression in a man or woman may be asking one or both of you to look at and change aspects of a relationship which are less than useful. It can easily be seen how changes in a partnership after a birth contribute to isolation and depression, especially if there are shaky areas in the partnership already. Expressing dissatisfactions is more useful than suffering in silence and increasingly growing apart, even if this causes pain and difficulty at a time when depression is affecting one or both of you.

Men and depression – loss

Although the postnatal hormonal question doesn't apply to men, they can suffer depression from the same causes as women: a previous history of depression, social and emotional pressure, the stress of adapting to parenthood, and so on. Just as having a baby means that a woman may need to come to terms with loss of freedom, youth and spontaneity, so men may need to go through a similar grieving experience. Men may still tend to have more actual freedom than women in this respect; this doesn't stop them experiencing regret at how much they are tied down.

Mark would talk about his 'long-lost bachelor days', when he would lie in late, live on Indian takeaways, see a wide circle of friends, and stay up until the small hours. Although his remarks were meant to be humorous, they held a large core of truth. Relations with Antonia were also complicated by their lack of sex life; for this reason (guilt at denying him, and fear that he might make demands) Antonia was more than happy to see Mark go out. He enjoyed his 'escapes', but still felt he was allowed out 'on a lead'.

For men just as for women, the arrival of a baby means a sea change – 'being under house arrest', as one father put it. As Mark's story indicates, he also loses his previous exclusive relationship with the woman, just as she does with him. This may not even be jealousy of the baby so much as a farewell to the more romantic elements of the relationship which are bound up with freedom.

Like women, men also have to part with fantasies of fatherhood and of the baby. As already stated, their self-image as a father may be even vaguer than a woman's self-image as a mother. It may also not be operational until the child is older! That is, many men visualize themselves playing with a child who can run about, a vision which has nothing to do with the helpless dependency of the newborn. And if there are problems such as colic in the first months of life, this can be just as hard on a father as on a mother. As Suzanne's husband, Rod, put it:

'The baby cried such a lot, it was bad for Suzanne, but it nearly drove me berserk. I would just walk out and leave her there to deal with it. I know it was bad and immature but it was the only way I could cope. I thought this little kid was going to come home and sit on my lap and we'd look at a book together or something. When I actually saw the baby, and heard it crying, it was so small and helpless, it was terrifying.'

73

This kind of initial disillusion is a common contribution to the mild or moderate kind of depression which men go through after a birth. Men may expect their partners to cope better than they do, and may feel anger and frustration at their partner's depression. Initial sympathy can soon be drained as the woman continues to be depressed.

Another point is disappointment over the sex of the child. Surveys have proved again and again that many men do still want a son, even if they don't always want to admit it. It has also been shown that men behave differently with boys even when they're babies, giving them more eye-to-eye contact and more stimulation generally.

Rod's first child was a girl, so people had spent the whole of Suzanne's pregnancy saying, 'Bound to be a boy this time'. When the second child proved to be a girl also, Rod could not conceal his disappointment, even in the delivery room.

Social pressure and your own private hopes can so easily dupe you into this kind of expectation, paving the way for disappointment. Sometimes too the women may even feel under pressure to fulfil her partner's hopes, impossible though this may be, experiencing irrational sadness or guilt when it doesn't happen. It can be hard to admit such inner processes because they are so far from our civilized ideas of ourselves. But, while they do exist, they should be seen in context as part of general fantasies of parenthood which are dispelled by the initial impact of a baby; time, getting to know the baby you actually have, do make such reactions fade significantly. Both men and women can also make efforts not to let sexual stereotyping creep into their treatment of their children, beginning even while they're still babies. Who knows, in this way, you might be cutting down on the possibility of depression after childbirth for the next generation.

The gap between the home and work: problems with new roles

A baby causes people to redefine their identity in the deepest sense, and both men and women can be confused about their new roles. Men in particular may find their new responsibilities difficult in that they don't have such a clearly defined role as the woman, especially at first when the baby is tiny, and especially if she's breastfeeding. There is a tendency for men to interpret these responsibilities externally instead of internally, to concentrate on being a good provider, to view their duties as economic. Fatherhood thus expresses itself as financial worry, propelling a man into a sometimes exaggerated role of breadwinner. For example, there's the

74

worker who does unnecessary overtime because it makes him feel more secure about his capacity to support a family (although in these days of recession it is by no means uncommon for employees to feel pressurized to do more than their fair share simply to keep their jobs). Work can be a source of security for men, somewhere where their identity is intact even if challenged outside by fatherhood. This deep absorption in work can cause distancing between partners: she feels he's not involved enough in babycare, he feels she doesn't appreciate how hard he's working outside the home.

There is also the question of exhaustion for men, as for women. If a man is working extra hard, and is perhaps also being woken up by the baby, he is also far more likely to come home tired and in need of love and support. If instead, he's met by an equally worn-out, depressed or irritable partner, he can easily react with resentment or depression.

Rod arrived home from work late to find Suzanne crying in morbid fear that the child would die a cot death. His exasperation was increased by the discovery that the baby was more than ready for her bottle, and that Suzanne hadn't sterilized any of the dirty ones. Lucy's husband Roger was under pressure at work and did resent her indifference to his needs. He felt his work was far more important than she could realize, and took to getting up at 5 a.m. in order to get in early. Not surprisingly, Roger himself became overtired and had bouts of black depression.

Men who are already feeling overburdened by the economic responsibility of parenthood may well lose patience with emotions which seem to have so little base in hard reality. Such reactions may be challenged by modern economic realities, where it may be only the woman who can get a job and the man is perforce left with the care of the baby. This may not help a man who has always viewed his responsibilities as financial ones. Depression because of unemployment is more widely appreciated than postnatal depression. Nevertheless, the monotony and loneliness of bringing up a baby can make a man depressed, just as they do a woman.

Depression or not, a baby means less money anyway and creates a work dilemma for one partner at least, usually the woman. It can certainly be a good time to re-examine ideas about money: are you actually badly off? Or are you being influenced by a general climate of economic fear? Could a working father be more involved with the baby? Is work a refuge, perhaps too much so? Money to use in order to meet needs is one matter; money as a more nebulous force, a source of identity and personal power, is another. Differentiating between them may help take some of the pressure off and get to the root of insecurities which may express themselves financially.

Low libido

Lack of interest in sexual relations, one of the most common symptoms of postnatal depression, is also one of the last to lift. In this respect, it can be a prime creator of jealousy and hurt in a man who feels rejected by his wife's lack of interest. However, a man's libido can also be altered by the arrival of a baby: he may be put off sex by having seen the birth and his wife suffering pain. There may also be the fear of conceiving again, especially if the woman has not yet been able to arrange contraception. Fatigue, the way energy is absorbed by the baby and by work, can play a part also. All this can add to depression; it can lead you to feel that a major part of your identity has dropped away, perhaps to worry about how normal it is, even to feel that you're the only ones who are going through this. There is social pressure always to be sexually available and active, and it is important to stand up to this, to take physical intimacy at your own pace. Many couples are forced to review their physical relationship for quite some time after a baby.

Helping someone with postnatal depression

If you are reading this book it may be because you know someone who has changed radically after having a baby, rather than because you yourself are a sufferer. Although this chapter is addressed to partners, the following section can also apply to anyone else who is close to the woman, such as a parent or friend, who wants to know how best to help.

It is deeply distressing to feel that the person you have known and loved until now has somehow gone away, to be replaced by a sad, angry stranger. But there is every chance of recovery, even if this means a trying period for anyone close to the woman. Your previous relationship is still valid, whether it was as partners, friends or family members. The arrival of the baby – or rather the depression – may seem to have flung that relationship into chaos, but it will settle down again in time.

As a general rule, it may help if you can think of her as someone who isn't well, or as a child whose behaviour you are reinforcing with praise rather than blame. Do your best to give lots of encouragement, to ignore the undone housework, her neglected appearance; do try also not to respond to the irritability in kind. Any kind of sickness needs vast reserves of patience and energy, and mental illness is no exception. It can be very draining living with someone whom you feel you constantly have to bolster up. So don't try to do too much. And bear in mind that restraint may sometimes be the least tiring option all round. If in doubt, try saying nothing rather than coming out with a critical or stinging comment.

Identifying postnatal depression

The main symptoms are set out in chapter 1, but here is a quick checklist of what to look for:

- any worrying changes in personality;
- easy crying, anger and irritability;
- tension, anxiety or panic;
- guilt, self-hatred;
- lethargy, constantly feeling ill;
- eating, drinking or sleeping disorders;
- low libido;
- poor memory or concentration;
- negative ideas about the baby.

Run together like this, it sounds overwhelming, although the woman is not likely to suffer from all these symptoms.

Identifying puerperal psychosis

Puerperal psychosis, much rarer, tends to occur just after the birth. The woman is much more obviously detached from reality, and may be over-excited or manic, very deeply depressed, or suffering from visual or auditory delusions (see chapter 2). If you think the woman is suffering from puerperal psychosis, get medical help immediately.

Suicide threats

Do not ignore or brush away suicide threats: they are a drastic but valid way of communicating how a woman is really feeling. It doesn't mean she is necessarily going to act on them but, sadly, postnatal depression can end this way. Try not to leave the woman alone – arrange for family or friends to stay for a while. Do encourage her to talk about her feelings as much as possible and also to seek her doctor's advice. Go with her and do not hesitate to get a second opinion if you're dissatisfied.

Maintaining detachment

It will not help if you allow yourself to be sucked into the woman's depression, although it can be difficult completely to avoid being affected. However, there is only so much you can do and you should not allow yourself to shoulder too much responsibility for the way she feels.

You may have to let go of the hope that you personally can effect a cure by your efforts. This may not always be possible; you can help, but you can't perform magic, and it may be necessary to call on a doctor or other outside help at some point. You may feel that this is a slur on someone who cares for the woman, a mark of failure, but you really cannot shoulder her whole burden yourself. Indeed, persuading the woman to seek professional help or other support could be one of the most valuable parts of the care you give her. Some therapy groups have a jargon which refers to 'enabling'. This is when a supportive friend is giving the depressed person permission to continue along the same lines, instead of helping her to change, because it makes them feel more powerful. While you may not exactly be doing this, you may need consciously to work on keeping some emotional distance from the woman, as well as persuading her to seek other help.

It can also be difficult listening to someone who seems to ask for support and yet reject it, a common message from a depressed person. Either way, know your limitations; it is exhausting trying to support a depressed person for long periods of time, and there *is* help for women with postnatal depression.

Take care of your own life

Meanwhile, and especially if you're a partner, you need to take what care you can of your own life, to keep up with friends, to look after your health, to go out together if possible. Of course, everyone's life is turned upside down by the arrival of a baby, but if your wife or girlfriend is depressed, there's even more than the usual need to get out of the house without the baby at least occasionally. The woman may just feel too low to accompany you, however. Don't press the point; if you can, at least get out on your own for now.

Accept her as she is

You also need to consider your own theories about what has caused the depression, whether you secretly or openly feel the woman should be able to 'snap out of it', and other possible prejudices. The view that a woman with a healthy baby 'should' be contented goes very deep in us, and evidence to the contrary is deeply disturbing. Her condition has to be accepted for what it is before you can begin to help. It won't be helpful if you preface your attempts with, 'But surely you've everything you ever wanted to make you happy', or, 'Do I have to listen to you moaning *again*!' Difficult though it can be to maintain sympathy and empathy during this draining time, it is easier if you can keep an open mind and give up the struggle to feel that she ought somehow to be different – more capable, stronger, more contented. Certainly, don't feel that it's your responsibility to make her change; absolve yourself from blame.

There's also the psychological see-saw which can take place between two people, especially partners or family members, whereby the down position of one automatically brings the other one up. It is an all too human reaction, on seeing someone in misery, to let the latent bully or prig surface. There's such a temptation to say, 'It's all your fault, and I'd never let myself get into such a mess.' So try to set aside jostles for power until the woman is stronger and it's a fair fight again! For now, you want to avoid making the woman feel even more guilty by nagging or lecturing.

Don't try to talk her out of it

Classic advice given to those who have to deal with postnatal depression (or indeed any depression) is not to try and reason with the woman. If depression were caused by faulty reasoning, the woman could probably have argued herself out of it long ago. She may indeed need to talk at length in order to recover, and to talk *honestly* about her feelings of fear or anger, without you rejecting such emotions. The safer you are as a person to listen, the more good it will do. She will talk far less freely if she senses that you are shocked or outraged at her attitude to motherhood. Really listening can be hard – it's so tempting to jump in halfway with solutions and suggestions – but do your best just to let her talk, dropping in the odd word to show you understand.

Acting as a buffer

How far should you shield the woman from the outside world? If a woman has postnatal depression, it's a time when support from family and friends may be very welcome, indeed necessary. Yet the woman may just not have the resources to cope with too many visitors, upsetting family situations, or people who are readier with criticism than support. In the same way, the woman may not be able to face looking at bills or bank statements or other realities of life. You may need to do some thinking for her, to discourage her from seeing people who do bring her down, and so on. Again, it can help if you think of her as being ill, and remember that some days will be better than others. It is highly probable that one day, when feeling stronger, she will be ready to take her share of responsibilities you may have been handling. Bear this in mind because you can get used to looking after everything, and may even find it hard to let go when the time comes. Be prepared for the woman to get well again.

You and the baby

Practical help with babycare can be one of the most useful things you can do for a woman who is feeling down after childbirth. Many fathers are keen to help in terms of doing something extra with the child – taking her out for a walk, sitting with her in the garden – but then hand her back when it's time for a feed or nappy change. What many women want, and don't get, is help with the boring, routine chores – giving a bottle, bathing, looking after other children and, especially, putting to bed, a time when the woman is likely to be even more tired. Some fathers hesitate to get involved in this way because they feel it's the mother's domain, or because they're scared of the baby's tiny size and general unpredictability. But one positive side effect of a mother's depression is that it *can* allow a closer relationship between the baby and his father, grandparent or other family members or friends. After all, in other cultures children are brought up within such a close-knit family group that they may feel they have three or four mothers.

If the woman is very depressed, you may have to take even more responsibility for the well-being of the child. It is hard, but don't let her remain alone with the baby if you feel there is the least doubt of her ability to care for it properly. If you suspect that she is in a condition to harm the baby, make sure she has someone with her all the time until she is really on the road to recovery. The same applies if you fear that she will harm herself. It is devastating to have such suspicions about someone you love, but try and separate the person from the mental illness, to see the one as a victim of the other. This deep depression does not mean that the woman cannot eventually become a good mother.

Looking after her

Postnatal depression means the woman may not be able to care for herself as effectively as before: she may forget to eat, for example, and won't care as much about the way she looks. Try and make sure that the woman is eating regularly; if she can't manage meals, little snacks every few hours are just as good if not better. If you take over the shopping, it might be easier to plan in terms of such snacks instead of meals for a while, especially if you aren't a great cook or don't have time to prepare a full meal. Useful items include savoury biscuits such as rice or oats, dried fruits, nuts and seeds, plenty of fresh fruit, fruit or vegetable juices, low-fat cheeses. Alcohol, chocolate, sweets and cakes may be all right in moderation but don't fall into the trap of using them as treats to try and make her feel better!

A depressed woman may have a great need for sleep – let her do so when possible. A good nap will probably help much more than you sitting down to thrash it all out yet again. If you're a partner, why not lie down too; if her libido is low, as is likely, staying close physically can be very reassuring for her and helps maintain closeness. Fathers too can suffer interrupted sleep even if they're not getting up for the baby, so extra rest can be useful all round.

Finally, you can help by encouraging the woman to contact a self-help group (see Useful Addresses) or accompanying her and the baby to a group meeting or even to see friends if she feels she can't manage alone.

Help with chores

Help with everyday tasks can be one of the most practical ways to offer help: for example, hanging out the daily wash in the mornings before going to work, or washing up the breakfast things, or taking the baby for ten minutes while the woman gets dressed. Try and see that the woman doesn't exhaust herself with heavy housework in the first six weeks after the birth, especially if she had a caesarean, as the tummy muscles need time to recover.

Friends or other family can be of great help in this kind of day-to-day routine – bringing over meals or offering to cook, helping with housework or shopping, picking up older children from school. People sometimes hesitate to offer help because they are nervous of intruding or because they are waiting to be asked. So do rope them in and make sure that passing visitors do something to help too.

You might also like to consider having some sort of paid or live-in help: for example, an au pair isn't necessarily an expensive middle-class luxury. But do think hard before having someone else in the house at this delicate time. Will the company help the woman or is it more likely to drive you all mad? Is it fair to ask someone to stay if the woman is very depressed? And it goes without saying that the outside help must be reliable. Go to a good agency; don't rely on friends of friends unless you're absolutely sure you're doing the right thing.

The future

It is classic advice in times of such turmoil to defer making major decisions such as moving house until matters have really settled down again, especially as the woman may be quite disinterested in any projects. But you may need to make a distinction between plans dating from before the birth and new plans. For example, if you were planning to move before the baby arrived, it may be better to go ahead, especially if you're moving from a small to a larger place where everyone will have more space. Nor is it always possible to put things on hold. However, bear in mind that you may be making the decisions on your own if the woman is very depressed and unable to take a real interest in what's going on.

One point where you could usefully suspend judgement is in the matter of having another child. That is, don't let this experience with

81

postnatal depression put you off expanding your family, at least not until you've had a chance to talk everything over in the months to come. Having postnatal depression once doesn't mean the woman will have it again; it is possible to take preventative care and to be alert for a recurrence another time around.

8

Help From Your Doctor

Postnatal depression has sometimes been described as the number one complication following childbirth. Given this, exactly what treatment is available for women? While it may not be a set medical condition in the way that measles is, your doctor may still be able to help. For many women too, the local GP will be the first port of call – because your depression may be fuelled by a physical condition such as anaemia, or may express itself in constant tension headaches or a fear of cancer, or simply because you don't know where else to turn. Women with postnatal depression consult their doctors for many reasons, which is why this chapter focuses on this subject. The next chapter deals with other kinds of help, with the emphasis on how you can help yourself.

First, before seeking help, it's important to remember that there is no one answer which works for everyone. You may need a combination of help from more than one source; for example, perhaps your husband prods you into seeing the doctor, who in turn passes you on to a postnatal support group. Sometimes, too, when the depression is probed, you encounter underlying problems, such as chronic overweight or a smoking habit, which will entail finding yet another kind of help. Other kinds of emotional and psychiatric disorders might need more specialized professional help. Last but by no means least, you shouldn't forget the sort of help from family and friends that sometimes takes the baby off your hands and enables you to rest!

It can be quite difficult for mothers, who may feel they are supposed to be the ones doing the caring, to come forward and admit they need to be cared for too. By now, you may have been struggling on alone for some time, and feel reluctant to admit that help is needed. In addition, when it comes to a mother with a small child seeking professional help, there is in this country a widespread mistrust of professional authority. In areas where the borderline between health and babycare might be blurred, there's that unspoken fear that if you confess to feeling ill or unconfident about some aspect of motherhood, 'They might take the baby away'. Unfortunately, the extremely poor reputation of social workers in this country has to some extent coloured people's perception of the service which should be making families' lives easier. This means that mothers can deprive themselves of available help because they are too scared to go to the doctor, and too worried about how they will be perceived if they confess to needing it. Such a deep mistrust can of course be part of the depression itself. But to ask for support doesn't mean you have to become totally passive, to accept what 'They' dole out without a murmur. To take an extreme example, some families who have been unjustly accused of ill-treating a child have even successfully sued their local authority.

Speaking more generally, you know yourself and your baby best, and it is very important that you should feel happy about anything which is done, or if not happy, that you should be convinced at depth that this is best. To be depressed after childbirth does not mean you give up all your rights as a citizen and all your powers of independent thought and feeling.

You and your doctor

The response you meet at your doctor's will vary according to the personality of the man or woman attending you, how aware he or she is of postnatal depression, and the nature of your own depression. Don't forget that you always have the right to a second opinion. GPs are certainly much more alert to the possibility of postnatal depression than they used to be, but on the patients' side, it still generally seems to be felt that the postnatal medical machine is geared up primarily for the baby's physical well-being, rather than for the mother.

The six-week check up does sometimes give doctors a chance to ask after the emotional as well as the physical well-being of the mothers, though this may miss the kind of depression which starts later on. Nor does everyone find this helpful.

Suzanne's GP asked her quite bluntly, 'Have you been depressed?' Her reaction was an automatic 'No'. She felt that although the question was designed to get her off guard and surprise her into the truth, it missed her because, as she said, 'I didn't know what depression was and I didn't know I was depressed. If he'd asked, "How are you feeling? How are you coping?" he would have got quite a different response.'

However, if this kind of question is asked, it does present a useful chance to ask about further treatment for depression should you decide you need it. You don't have to commit yourself right now if you don't want to; sometimes it can be enough just to know that help is there if you need it. Meanwhile, it can be worth finding out your doctor's attitude, and if you feel you do want help, why not take up the offer right away and save yourself more misery in the future?

Given that your depression is diagnosed, what can your doctor offer you to help it get better? Again, this varies. Some doctors may feel that

84

you don't really need treatment as such, and that their individual support is enough to get you through this tricky patch. This was Marcia's experience.

'My GP was a young man, very recently qualified, who just sort of talked me through it. He said it was all hormonal and I would just have to wait until it all settled down again. I asked if he'd give me something to help me sleep and he said I didn't really need it – he was reluctant to prescribe anything. He was very kind and supportive and I got better very gradually over about fifteen months. But I do feel that fifteen months without proper sleep is a long time and I wonder if I might have got better more quickly with some medication.'

If you do disagree with what your doctor is saying, don't forget that you do have the right to protest. For example, in Marcia's case, it is quite possible that her doctor just didn't realize the anguish of difficult nights week after week, because he wasn't told clearly enough. Compromises are always possible: in this case, perhaps, a strictly limited course of medication. Because of this sort of difficulty in communication, it is a good idea to make a list of your most troublesome symptoms before you go in. It is so easy to become flustered when faced with the doctor and not say what you meant to say.

What about anti-depressants? You may be reluctant to accept these for fear of addiction and doctors are certainly more cautious about prescribing them these days. However, there are types of anti-depressant which are not addictive. It may take a few different prescriptions before you find the right one for you, and they can take a while to work. You may also need to ask your doctor about any side-effects such as dry mouth or blurred vision. Some mothers also worry about taking medication if they are breastfeeding. Tiny amounts of whatever you consume do pass to the baby through breastmilk, and drugs such as marijuana and alcohol have been shown to affect breastfed babies. Unfortunately, not that much research has been done on the effects of anti-depressants on breastfed babies. You can certainly make this another question to discuss with your doctor, depending on which anti-depressant you are prescribed. If you do decide to go ahead with breastfeeding while taking anti-depressants, you could also keep a diary of your baby's behaviour to monitor any changes after you have taken any medication (as anti-depressants take a few weeks to work, you should allow the same amount of time in which to note any effects).

This said, postnatal depression may present one time in your life when it pays to be pragmatic about medication, to regard it as a temporary help to get you out of the black hole. Again, trust in your doctor is needed –

trust that he isn't 'fobbing you off' with a few pills, but will be there if needed when you stop taking the medicine too.

Referral

Sometimes your doctor may decide that you need further help, or this may be a decision which you reach together. Consider carefully the options your doctor puts before you; you can go away and think about it before deciding.

How your doctor refers you depends on what your doctor thinks lies behind your depression. The hormonal question raised by Marcia's case is described more fully below under 'Depression and hormonal treatment', and although this whole issue is still controversial and under-researched some doctors do offer this kind of treatment.

If your depression is severe, you may be taken into hospital for a while. Your doctor may also recommend psychiatric care – group or individual therapy led by an analyst. Otherwise, some local practices hold postnatal support groups or child management sessions, or have links with the local hospital where this kind of support may also be available. Other doctors will recommend that you get in touch with the Association for Postnatal Illness (see below and Useful Addresses) or other local groups. Yet others will have more general suggestions, such as going to local mother and toddler sessions or playgroups where you can meet other mothers. It does depend partly on just how depressed you are, and how well you've managed to communicate your condition, as well as the attitude of the doctor attending you.

More about counselling

Counselling has been mentioned a number of times during this book – but what exactly is it, what good is it likely to do you, and how do you get it?

Briefly, counselling should provide an environment in which it is safe for you to talk over your problems freely. You may not actually receive 'counselling' as such – that is, you may not get direct advice which will change your life, nor does counselling always provide crystal-clear solutions to your problems. But with a skilled counsellor's help you should be able to talk your way through to increased acceptance of what has happened. It can often be easier for someone else to hear what you are really saying – to pick up on unconscious repetitions, to reflect back to you more clearly matters of which you may only be half aware. For example, if your depression is mixed up with ambivalent feelings towards your baby, as you talk about your guilt and confusion a counsellor might pick up on a resentment towards your partner, which perhaps stems, in turn, from an unresolved conflict with your own parents. Counselling may not need to probe back as far as this; it may just be a matter of you talking about the stresses of your present life – a crying baby, perhaps, or lack of money, or just the general feeling of being overwhelmed and exhausted. The main thing is that you be as open as you possibly can – to speak as you really feel, not as you 'ought' to feel. This is not always easy; in some respects, it's a skill, which has to be learned like other skills. The counsellor is there to help you learn.

Types of counselling vary. Some people have found their doctor and health visitor to be great sources of support, meeting them every week or fortnight to discuss progress. In-depth psychiatric counselling may be recommended by your doctor if he or she feels your depression is more serious. For other women, a voluntary counsellor from the Association for Postnatal Illness may be more helpful – another woman who has been through postnatal depression. The Association works in the first instance by means of telephone support – if you ring, a volunteer will shortly call you back, and you can take it from there. In other organizations there are specialized counsellors for problems such as alcohol or drug addiction, or marriage or relationship problems. Your doctor can pass you on to professional counsellors, or you may find a lay counsellor (someone who's had the problem) from a support group more useful, or you may want to approach a marriage guidance association (see Useful Addresses). Group counselling can be useful for some people – again, your doctor may be able to tell you about local postnatal support groups, or you could contact your local hospital for information.

Depression and hormonal treatment

By no means all doctors accept the theory that a drop in hormone levels after the birth causes postnatal depression, even if they agree that the initial baby blues are due to hormonal changes in the body. This is partly because, traditionally, postnatal depression has been viewed as a psychiatric disorder, and partly because there is no overwhelming body of scientific evidence to convince orthodox medical opinion of the hormonal theory. Some doctors may however be willing to make room for hormonal influences, although they may also want to take psychological or social factors into consideration. While some may treat the depression with injections of progesterone, others may prefer simply to leave the body to regain its own balance.

Certainly, women *have* been helped by hormone treatment, so you might wonder why it isn't routinely offered to all with postnatal depression. Unfortunately it isn't that simple. It isn't just that there is no evidence that all cases of postnatal depression are caused by hormonal upset, or that some doctors place more emphasis on psychiatric or physical causes. This touches on a problem which has haunted the field of postnatal depression – misdiagnosis or even failure to diagnose. The woman referred for in-depth psychiatric treatment turns out to be suffering from sheer loneliness; the one given anti-depressants desperately needs to talk to someone at length about some trauma in her past. The risk with hormonal treatment is that it may leave underlying psychological/emotional problems untouched. The eagerness to find a physical cause for a distressing disorder, and then something to cure it, is understandable. What a relief to feel that it's all physical and that you're not going mad after all! But even without an underlying mental or emotional problem, you may find that hormone treatment needs to be backed up by other kinds of support. By the time you try hormonal treatment, you may have been through so much that medical care may just not be enough. There may be a need to talk in depth to a counsellor, so do ask for extra support if you feel that what's been prescribed isn't enough. Practical and emotional problems may well have built up during the weeks and months of your depression, which an injection cannot cure.

In addition, research is still far from complete on what constitutes normal hormone levels for women. So far it seems that because everyone needs slightly different amounts of hormones there is no one hormonal medication which will work for everyone, though some doctors have gone some way towards standardizing treatments of progesterone injections. In other words, women can't be offered hormonal treatment in the way they are an anti-rubella jab. Individual tests are necessary to find the right balance of hormones to give, and this testing is delicate, costly and by no means available everywhere in Britain.

To sum up, hormonal treatment, although promising valuable results, cannot be viewed in isolation as a kind of wonder treatment. But, even those who don't believe in the hormonal theory feel it is important as a popular myth, because it shows how people are thinking and what they are willing to believe. It also shows how much women need serious 'scientific' recognition of postnatal depression and corresponding treatment.

The Pill

'The depression really took off when I was put back on the Pill. With what I now know about postnatal depression, I'm really cross about my GP's ignorance.'

Lucy's experience applies to other women who have found that they no longer seem to be able to take their usual contraceptive pill because it makes them so much more depressed. This is linked with the hormonal theory: it is thought that the artificial hormone in the pill, progestogen, lowers a woman's natural progesterone, so increasing the chance of depression. Another result is a lower libido, increasing what's viewed as a symptom of postnatal depression anyway.

It's also worth bearing in mind that the Pill can lower levels of vitamin B_6. At a time when mothers may still be breastfeeding, certainly still running round after a new baby, they may well be more run down than usual, so that even a slight lowering of vitamin levels may have more effect than it might otherwise have had.

There is also the possibility that contraception offers permission to become sexually viable again in a way which a depressed mother may just not feel ready for. All in all, it may be worth discussing other forms of contraception with your doctor for now, especially if you aren't very sexually active. A word of warning – don't rely on breastfeeding as a contraceptive!

Pre-menstrual syndrome

It might seem odd to read about pre-menstrual syndrome in a book devoted to postnatal depression, but your doctor may ask you about this as certain links have been found between both conditions. The main one is that sufferers from pre-menstrual syndrome experience a similar drop in progesterone. Some research also seems to indicate that some women who have suffered from postnatal depression go on to develop pre-menstrual syndrome for the first time; in fact, the one can merge into the other as time goes on after the birth and your periods return. You can help your doctor and yourself gain a clearer idea of whether this is so by keeping a diary of your pre-menstrual tension, and by noting any particular effects which occur after you give up breastfeeding and your periods return.

Physical checks

Your doctor may also need to perform physical examinations depending on what you feel is wrong. It is worth checking out physical symptoms after a birth. They are not always depression in disguise, and sometimes may contribute to depression by making you feel rundown or ill.

For example, the discomfort or pain of a uterine prolapse can be wearing and so contribute to depression. Even minor conditions, such as stress incontinence, can drastically affect your image of yourself because of the extra sensitivity you feel in depression. Normally the body does an amazing job at adjusting after a pregnancy and birth, but there are areas where the effects may be longer-lasting. And some women take longer than others to pull together again after birth.

Antonia felt that the impact of pregnancy and birth had left her a stranger in her body. She was left with all sorts of common minor complaints which, taken together, irritated her and made her feel rather defeated.

'My varicose veins hung around and I always thought only old ladies had them, I was overweight and couldn't get rid of it, every time I ran up the stairs I leaked urine, I got backache a lot, I had chronic conjunctivitis. Every bug that was going, I got – colds, tummy bugs, flu, the lot. I felt as if I was falling apart!'

Not feeling physically at ease can mirror the emotional discomfort you are also going through. Sometimes too you may be afraid that the minor complaints indicate real underlying problems, so if nothing else your GP can eliminate worry about your condition by a physical examination. It must also be pointed out that many parents who aren't depressed also suffer numerous little ailments. It is natural to be more rundown when you are looking after a demanding infant and picking up all the germs she may collect from mother and toddler groups. All in all, birth may well leave you with physical after-effects which can last some time and need the doctor's attention, the more so if you are depressed. This section focuses on the type of condition where even a little medical help may be appropriate. More general advice on such matters as diet and exercise can be found in the next chapter. So don't be afraid to ask your doctor for any help you need during this time. It is quite common to need the doctor more often after a birth anyway – it won't last for ever. As your depression improves, the chances are that one day you'll suddenly realize you haven't been down to the surgery for months.

Anaemia

If you lost blood during the birth – for example with a caesarean or haemorrhage – you may be left with anaemia, which can cause exhaustion and so play a significant part in postnatal depression. Doctors usually try and make good blood loss with a transfusion or iron tablets and either of these may have been offered while you were still in hospital. Even so, these may not have been enough, especially if some time has gone by and your periods have returned. It may well be worth asking your doctor to check you out for anaemia if you feel very exhausted, because it is so common and so easily put right. A simple blood test reveals the presence of anaemia and a course of iron pills will be prescribed. Apart from feeling extremely tired, you may also experience other symptoms such as pallor, breathlessness on slight exertion, and irritability.

Thyroid deficiency

Another test your doctor might perform is to check that your thyroid is working properly. The thryoid produces a hormone which influences the speed at which the body works. If in the upheaval following the birth the thyroid isn't producing enough of this hormone, exhaustion can be one result, leading perhaps to depression. Other symptoms include feeling cold, dry skin, lank hair which falls our easily (though don't forget that you do tend to lose hair after a birth which only grows back after some months), a slow pulse, and the tendency to fall asleep at any time. Your doctor can check your pulse rate and do a blood test to look for thyroid deficiency, which is easily cured with a course of medication. You shouldn't need this medication for ever, as the body usually adjusts back in time.

Breast problems

Cracked nipples, mastitis or other breast infections are more likely to occur in the first month or two, before breastfeeding is really established. But such problems can come later on too, and may just be the last straw if you're already run down and tired, fed up of breastfeeding anyway, and have a baby you find difficult to feed. At this point it is very easy to give up. If this happens when you would perhaps rather have continued, it can be damaging to your confidence. Breastfeeding is a highly emotive issue and one where women can all too easily feel they've failed – feelings which can affect your image of yourself as a mother and contribute to depression. But do consult your doctor about breastfeeding if it continues to be very painful, if you have a sharp shooting pain in your nipples, redness or soreness in your breasts, pus coming from the nipples and/or a temperature. Any of these may mean the possibility of a breast infection; breast lumps also need investigation. An infection is easily cured by antibiotics (don't forget that the antibiotics may make you feel more tired than usual). Your doctor or health visitor, or a support group, may also be able to advise you on feeding difficulties (see Useful Addresses).

Prolapse of the uterus

This is when the pelvic floor muscles, stretched by delivery, allow the tip of the uterus to protrude into the vagina, causing a heavy, dragging or painful feeling. If this hasn't gone too far, the cure is disciplined use of the pelvic floor exercises (clenching your muscles as if to stop the flow of urine). Otherwise, this condition may need surgical treatment.

Cervical erosion

An ulcer on the tip of the cervix, a cervical erosion is very common in pregnancy and may persist after delivery, causing more vaginal discharge than normal. If it doesn't heal up on its own, minor surgery may be recommended. The extra discharge can be worrying, especially as it's occasionally smeared with a slight amount of blood; your doctor can reassure you.

Stress incontinence

If you're not feeling too good about yourself, it can be horrifying to feel that your control over your bladder has gone, especially in public. After a birth, some women find that a small amount of urine escapes when they run, jump, laugh, or sneeze. Again, the cure is use of the pelvic floor exercises.

Constipation/anal fissure

Constipation is normal after a birth but can be painful and stressful, especially if an anal fissure or tiny crack has developed. Although a fissure can last for weeks untreated, it can be healed quite easily with prescribed lubricant, so don't suffer in silence!

Piles and/or varicose veins

These may develop during pregnancy or at delivery and usually heal up soon afterwards; if they persist, however, you may need to ask your doctor for further treatment as both can be painful, even debilitating. Untreated piles for example can lead to anaemia, while painful varicose veins may be enough to stop you trying to break out of your isolation and walk a few streets to visit another mother.

Weight gain

One school of thought cites weight gain as a symptom of postnatal depression, with hormonal links. Certainly, your doctor may be able to help you with a weight problem – if you feel you aren't losing weight fast enough after the birth or have even put on more. He will probably advise against strict dieting, certainly in the early weeks, and can reassure you that some weight gain is quite normal after birth to prepare the body for breastfeeding. Quite often, a mixture of breastfeeding, activity and sensible eating will work wonders with post-pregnancy weight gain, but if your depression is preventing you from doing any of these, do ask your doctor for more help. Don't be fobbed off with reassurance if this problem is worrying you; but do try to keep a realistic balance when looking at it.

Different visits, different symptoms?

It can sometimes be difficult to decide what you want to ask your doctor about. That dry skin which has developed? That worrying ache in your tummy or your heart? The fact that you can't remember the last time you had a good night's sleep? Can you say, 'I feel very depressed *and* I have a load of physical things which don't feel right'?

Some women do experience shifting symptoms: they are reassured about their heart condition only to return a month later with fears about cancer. When physical symptoms do mask depression, it isn't always easy to be aware of the deep anxiety which may be behind them. However, you shouldn't try and put up with illness or discomfort because you suspect that you are fabricating it all. As this chapter has tried to show, your doctor can genuinely help with a number of genuine complaints. It isn't your fault if you do have to go back a few times. It can also be easy for a depressed mother to put off going to the doctor, so that when she does go she has quite a list of complaints which have been building up over the months. You may also be confused about whether you are seeking help for postnatal depression or for postnatal physical disorders, and it may not always be possible to sort out how far the two may be separate or interlinked. Either way, it helps to accept that you may need treatment for both – and that you can always return if you feel that one visit is not enough to cure what can be a complex condition where the links and dividing points between mental and physical aren't always clear. So don't suffer in silence, and don't rely on self-diagnosis – your doctor spent many years training in order to help people just like you!

9

How to Help Yourself

In postnatal depression, as in other low times in life, there is a balance between accepting outside help and moving forwards alone. The care you give yourself may seem pointless when you're really low but is actually very important. Looking after yourself is part of the adult responsibilities you assume when you have a baby, although the awareness of this should not be used as a stick to beat yourself with when depressed. Indeed, the knowledge that you can't yet live up to your 'grown-up' role may well be adding to your depression. But this realization *can* be used as an incentive to look after yourself more if you feel you need that sort of justification: you can see self-care as mature, not selfish, in the best interests of the whole family as well as yourself. It may also help to remember that no one is ever totally mature!

It is also a psychological given that the inner motivation to help yourself is often more effective than outside support which is offered. In some ways, the impetus to get better has to come from you, even if you need the help of others to complete the cure. The thirsty person may still have to ask for water, even if someone else brings him or her the glass. Just as only you really know what a difference the baby has made to your life, so you are the only one who can really create your new identity so that it's comfortable for yourself. The care you give yourself is a mark of how much you value yourself – in the end the most solid assessment. Self-care is also an important statement about motherhood which can affect the quality of your life for some time to come, a statement that you're not prepared to be totally swallowed up by babycare. While you may need to depend on outside help for a while, ultimately it's your assessment of yourself that you live with. Remember that feelings of uselessness and unworthiness are a sign of depression, not a valid statement about the way you are.

So what is self-care? While its essence lies in an attitude, not actions, you may have to force yourself into actions at first: sometimes, feelings follow actions rather than the other way round. In other words, if you're too depressed to care one way or another about yourself, you need at some point to make the inner decision to care, whether that's communicated or not. On a down-to-earth note, self-care is sitting down with a snack and drink at regular intervals; it's taking half an hour's nap in the afternoon instead of worrying about the untidy bedroom; it's calling someone you can trust for a talk; it's putting the baby in a sling or pram and walking out on your bad temper and an unmanageable house and getting some fresh air; it's leaving the baby and a couple of bottles with your partner and going off to spend the night at a friend's.

If you are reading this book, it is likely that you already have some motivation towards helping yourself. Do your best to cherish it: any urge involving self-love is healthy in a depression where hatred of yourself may be the reigning emotion. Just a little self-help may go a long way towards pulling you out of the slough of misery which constitutes postnatal depression. Even picking up the phone to call a support group is a form of self-help, which is why such organizations are included in this chapter. Be prepared for the depression to put up many complex barriers if you do start to consider breaking out of it. For example, making a phone call sounds so easy, but you may be put off doing so for a long time by just the welter of emotions which have been making you so miserable: churning resentment, emptiness, perhaps a feeling that the woman at the other end will be a superior angel doling out help in a condescending way, or an earth mother who insists you learn to breastfeed properly before you're accepted. Such nuances are more likely to be in your imagination than anywhere else – it may help to know that many self-help groups are staffed by volunteers who have themselves been through the same experience as you. Also, some of the barriers can come from the feeling that, once you do reach out for help, things are likely to change, and the depression may have made you feel that you simply can't face anything new. Take it one step at a time: much of life is made up of small things and nobody is demanding dramatic changes of you overnight.

Establishing your priorities

In a life muddled by a baby and by depression it can seem as if there are no priorities: only a series of urgent and less urgent demands. Babycare and housework may be punctuated by worry about money, concern for your career or for your partner. You simply are not capable of managing all your worries at once. So put first yourself, your baby and any other children; then your partner; and then care of the house. The priorities are fluid when it comes to you and your family – sometimes the baby may need more care, sometimes other children, sometimes yourself. More tips on coping with the baby (and other children) are in the next chapter. Care of the house should really just be what tidiness you can manage, and food provision. For some, paid work will have to be a priority into which self-care is fitted as best it possibly can be.

Coping with tiredness –
rest, rest, rest!

'I'd say I lost a year, walking round in some twilight zone. I found I could keep going, physically, although I couldn't nap when my baby was asleep, as some of my friends did. I just went round like a zombie: apathetic, irritable, grey.'

Getting enough rest is possibly the most important thing in your life when you are suffering from postnatal depression. So many women report the type of feelings described by Suzanne above, and feeling absolutely wiped out is such a feature of postnatal depression that you must take heed of your need for rest if you are feeling far more tired than usual. You may need to let go and sleep a lot more: even if you can't sleep, you can still put your feet up.

Do have yourself checked for anaemia (see previous chapter). Otherwise do all you can to make it easier on yourself. Sit or lie down when the baby is asleep – *don't* fall into the classic trap of rushing around to do 'just one more' of the chores. Establish priorities and let the rest go. Clean one room such as the bathroom or kitchen; have a couple of chests or big boxes into which you can throw everything for a quick tidy up; cook one meal and do healthy snacks for the others.

If your partner doesn't like a less tidy house, you may need to explain how you are feeling and why it is important for you to rest; he can always do the washing-up himself or arrange for help with housework from a relative, friend or paid worker. In some ways you need to be quite ruthless when trying to help yourself – certainly don't regard yourself as there just to tidy the house or care for the baby. Acceptance is always a good starting-point for recovery from depression, so accept that you are tired without burdening yourself with extra 'shoulds'. Do your best to be aware of your physical needs and give in to them whenever you can.

Taking on too much

While on the subject of tiredness, there often comes a point a few months after the birth when the exhaustion peaks. It tends to come at a time when mothers feel they ought to have recovered from the birth by now, and start to do more. The danger with this is simply taking on too much, resulting in exhaustion, and this can be one reason why some mothers have depression some months after the birth. (This extra activity may also cause a drop in breast milk – see next chapter for more on breastfeeding.) There is the temptation to try and get out and about with the baby, to go and see friends, perhaps to take on some work. When none of these activities quite work out, it can be destructive to your confidence. That much-planned trip to the art gallery ends up as a fiasco, with you breastfeeding endlessly in the car; that trip to a friend's ends with the baby howling at the bus stop, no bus, and you feeling absolutely desperate (and naturally without money for a taxi). Unfortunately, one result is to become much more wary of going out at all, which can create even more isolation and so reinforce depression.

If you have found some sort of way of getting through the day and the week which works for you, stick to it until you feel really stronger. Don't be too tempted to expand or to push yourself. Focus on making more local contacts, which will stand you in good stead for months to come anyway. Don't feel you can never go anywhere because it's bound to be a disaster, but take it cautiously, or go further afield when you've got someone to accompany you for now.

Avoidance

Avoiding unpleasantness tends to be frowned on by our Puritan heritage, to be viewed as character-weakening. 'Do at least two things a day you don't want to do', runs the eager command from some self-help literature. In the throes of postnatal depression, however, there is a real case for ignoring all this and making a point of avoiding what you feel you can't handle. Don't do things out of a weary sense of duty: stick to what you really feel will do you good, and be easy on yourself. For the time being, allow yourself not to see people who irritate or drain you, or who make you feel bad about yourself. Don't force yourself to watch television or read the newspaper, to keep up with what are after all other people's private tragedies. You have enough on your plate, and besides, what can you do about it? It can sometimes be very difficult to keep your emotional balance when the 'poisonous whispers' strike, presenting themselves as final truths about life.

Tara had a friend who was a nurse, who talked to her about the worst of her cases. Tara had been feeling somewhat better, but these revelations preyed on her mind so much that, over a few weeks, she came to feel life was pointless as it all ended in sickness and death. She felt as if she'd been sheltered from a truth which was now inescapable, but kept it to herself until one evening, when it emerged in talk with her partner. He said at once, 'That sounds like deep depression to me. Why do you listen to her if it upsets you?' This immediately broke up Tara's 'final truth' and she was able to start taking a more balanced view of life again.

97

Be selfish and choose your company – don't be afraid to say no to meetings which you don't feel will boost you. And, while Tara's partner was supportive, don't worry if others don't always understand your feelings. If you need to talk more than your current support system can listen, there are many other mothers who have been through depression who can lend an ear (see below under 'Support groups').

'Polish your shoes'

In the same spirit, there is what's been called the 'polish your shoes' advice – doing any small task that will get you through a few minutes and avoid the desolation of having absolutely nothing to do. Done slowly and steadily these small tasks can bring quite a lot of order into your life as well as being therapeutic in their own right. But don't let this exercise escalate into a mad gallop through your accumulated tasks; it's much more beneficial if you can take it slowly, otherwise you risk getting caught up in a rush and exhausting yourself. You are always going to be interrupted by the baby. It is worth cultivating the art of being satisfied with little achievements – a wash put on, the nappy bucket emptied, tidying a drawer. Not very glamorous or interesting, perhaps, but more psychologically helpful than you might realize. In some cases, just getting the task done might be reward enough for you, but otherwise do give yourself a pat on the back when you've accomplished something. This could be no more than taking a moment to acknowledge what you've done, or it could be something more concrete, like allowing yourself to lie down and rest for ten minutes without feeling guilty. Nurturing yourself – 'babying' yourself if you like – is important.

Sensible eating

Many depressed mothers do lose their appetites. Try eating small meals or snacks at regular intervals; cooking elaborate meals is not for life with a baby unless you find it therapeutic and enjoy it. You could also keep a note of any effects certain foods may have on your mood. Try and avoid the instant appeal of a chocolate bar: go for fresh, light, appetizing snacks such as celery filled with cottage cheese, carrots grated with a shredding of onion and French dressing, apple and banana fruit salad with a handful of raisins and sunflower seeds. Do give some time to food preparation: chopping a cabbage may seem too fiddly but if approached in the right spirit can form part of the winding down process whereby you try and sit down and relax over your meal!

You might also find it easier to drink rather than eat more – vegetable soups (which can be frozen), fortified milk shakes (add dried milk, wheatgerm, fruit, etc.). Another tip if you've lost your appetite is to get someone else to cook for you or to use takeaways at least once a week: being bored or even repelled by your own cooking certainly doesn't help healthy eating. Also, try shopping somewhere different or choosing different items.

Conversely, food cravings sometimes form part of depression. Many breastfeeding mothers especially get extremely hungry and can't seem to 'fill up' without a bite of chocolate or a couple of biscuits at the end of a meal. In moderation, this isn't something to worry about: minor eating indulgences tend to correct themselves as you become stronger. You certainly don't want to add guilt over food to your other anxieties. Constant bingeing is another matter and should perhaps be one of the subjects you discuss with your doctor (see previous chapter). You might also find a support group useful.

Exercise

Exercise is a great mood-changer but it can be very difficult to get started when paralysed by depression. One obvious way to get more exercise is to join a postnatal exercise or swimming class – it's also a good way of meeting people – but this can require more organization and commitment than you have at present. (If you do join a class, make sure the organizer knows you have recently had a baby.) Try and incorporate more exercise into your life as it is right now instead of waiting until the mythical day when you'll take up that t'ai chi class down the road. Go for a walk with the baby; try four or five simple yoga exercises once a day while the baby's asleep; take the stairs at a run instead of a plod. In depression, it's often the effort of will involved in *starting* which is hardest. If nothing else, try and keep up your pelvic floor exercises for the first few months after the birth.

Work out your attitude to motherhood

Ambivalence about being a mother may contribute to your depression, so it can be helpful to get to the root of any psychological conflict about your new role. Write down your feelings in quiet moments when the baby's feeding or sleeping. Questions you might like to consider include: were both you and your partner equally happy about having a baby? Have you recently (in the last two years) undergone life stresses such as bereavement, work changes, moving house? Have you had a happy relationship with your own parents and especially your mother?

You could also think about specific areas of your life which mother-hood has changed: your health, your energy level, your sex drive, your career, your relationship with your partner, how much money you have to spend, how often you go out, how often you see your friends. Has the reality of the baby been very different from how you imagined it? Write down your fantasies of motherhood – how you feel it should be, as well as how it actually is. Be clear about any feelings of bitterness, loss and anger. In this way, you can pin-point areas of your life where you feel hardest hit, and start planning to do something about them. You may be surprised to find that sometimes it just needs a gesture, a symbol that you're not totally 'sunk in motherhood'.

Tara's list was topped by 'drab and boring image', so she bought some new clothes; even though she couldn't afford it, this was something she had to do. Lucy had imagined being warm and maternal but found she missed the intellectual stimulus of her job; as described earlier, part-time work helped restore her balance. Carrie was surprised by the amount of anger she discovered when writing an account of how she felt; eventually, she enjoyed taking out her aggression in a gym class.

Writing out how you feel is not going to make everything better overnight. Motherhood will remain imperfect, stressful perhaps, disappointing perhaps. But it needn't just be a case of finding yourself small consolation prizes such as a new dress or a class to make yourself feel better; as Lucy's work indicates, you can take this time to clarify more ambitious, long-term goals too which can merge with and complement motherhood, rather than being in conflict with it. Just because depression may have set you back for a while, there is no reason why you shouldn't plan to forge ahead again, if not in the immediate future, then at some point further on in your life.

Have your own money

Having your own money can give you a valuable sense of power in a depression where you may feel totally power*less* and overwhelmed. For some, a return to work may be the obvious answer, but it doesn't have to be huge sums: if nothing else, you can arrange that you are in a position to cash your child benefit each week. Measly though the sum is, it could cover say a book or magazine for yourself as well as a set of new vests for the baby if you feel guilty at spending it on yourself! Or it could buy help with the chores or a few hours' babysitting while you go out. Don't forget it is of more benefit to your baby to have a mother refreshed by a short absence than to have those new vests. Secondhand ones will keep him or her just as warm.

If you can't or don't want to go back to work, do find out if you are entitled to other benefits such as the Family Allowance (contact your local Department of Social Security). Also think about little ways to increase the cash flow: babysitting, car boot sales, and catering are some options. But don't take on such activities if you find they're a great strain and you end up irritable and harassed. While many women loathe having to ask their partners for money, a regular allowance for you may be the most practical arrangement for now. After all, if it was you going out to work and your husband staying at home (an arrangement increasingly forced on people by recession) you can bet he'd want his own money!

Have your own time

Time to yourself needs the co-operation of others and, if you're depressed, it can be much more difficult to face the demands of interacting with them. This can be especially true if you don't feel you're in a position to repay people who babysit for you. First, try and accept that you do need help: say yes to whoever offers because you can always pay them back later when you feel better. Second, try and realize that there will be some people for whom the term 'help' is inappropriate. Your partner and other family members need opportunities to get to know the baby; it is their right as well as perhaps their duty to share the baby and so 'help' you.

Ask your partner what time he can realistically spare: a few hours on Saturday morning, on a weekday evening? Rope in other relatives who have offered, however tepidly, to babysit; they will only be sitting watching TV or seeing their own friends if left to their own devices, and your need may be much greater than their need of such leisure for the moment. Once you've arranged your free time, don't go for mammoth excursions which will leave you shaky and stressed. Getting out of the house can be a major job for some women suffering from postnatal depression, so keep your outings easy at first. Go to the local swimming pool, the shops, the park, to the library (armed with a notebook in which to write down your feelings about postnatal depression), anywhere where you can just get away for a couple of hours without putting yourself under pressure to do something demanding or exciting.

Having your own time can also mean arranging complete short breaks from the family: a night spent at your own mother's or at a friend's, a day away with your partner. Don't neglect this if at all possible – even a short time away can leave you feeling surprisingly better.

Support groups and organizations

If you don't want to seek professional help, there are many support organizations for mothers. The main one for women with postnatal depression is the Association for Postnatal Illness, which has been a lifeline for many sufferers. Support is offered by volunteers from around the country, and the Association also offers information about postnatal depression. If you think you are suffering from postnatal depression, you can call or write to the Association (see Useful Addresses) who will then get a volunteer to call you back, and/or send you some literature which can help you identify more precisely how you are feeling. In the experience of those who work with the Association, the literature is also useful in that it helps your family and even your doctor understand better what is happening to you. Seeing it in black and white can make it more real to all concerned.

For many women, there is nothing quite as helpful as talking with someone who's been through the same experience as themselves, someone who understands. But, as explained at the start of this chapter, the depression itself can make it very hard for a mother to contact an association or group. You may feel that it's all too much trouble with a young baby, especially when you're so worn out. Or you may worry about the reception that you will get, or just feel too unworthy for anyone to want to talk to you, or that you have too many associated problems which are too complicated to solve. While you do need to break through all this in order to make that first phone call, it's also important to take any help at your pace. Many depressed women find it hard to leave the house, to get out and meet other people face to face. So don't worry if just talking on the phone is all you can manage – it may be all you need for now.

You may also feel that you want to tackle some other problem than postnatal depression, such as an over-eating or drinking problem. You may need to think about whether the support organization is addressing your central problem. Are you overdoing the chocolate biscuits because eating has always been a major problem, or because you're bored and lonely with no other new mothers to talk to? Was your drinking an existing problem which really took off after the baby arrived, or did the problem just spring up after the birth as part of a general depression? A phone call or two to different support organizations may help you get your ideas clearer; and do try to listen to feedback from family and friends who know you as you try to sort out the real central problem for which you need help first. Don't try and sort everything out at once: settle the central problem and the rest will gradually fall into place after it.

In approaching some groups you may encounter other difficulties: while groups for mothers tend to operate round nursery hours, with daytime meetings, other groups may be hard to get to because of your circumstances. For example, it can be hard for an exhausted, depressed mother to drag herself out in the evenings.

Marcia had an over-eating problem which she desperately wanted to tackle as she felt it contributed greatly to her depression. Her doctor initially had advised her not to diet but when the baby was a year old, she felt she couldn't bear being 'a fat old mum' any more. But her nearest support group met one evening a week at 8 p.m., a time when she was too tired to face going out. In addition, it was twenty minutes' drive away, and Marcia was not a confident driver, especially in her present state. She would also worry about whether the baby would wake and whether her partner could cope if she did.

All these problems have solutions of course. If you're worried about leaving the baby, your partner could learn how to give the baby a bottle, you could splash out on a minicab, or get your partner or a friend to drive you. It also depends on how desperate you are for the help: with a crippling drug problem, for example, it may be a case of having to have the help no matter what.

Finally, you may have specific problems related to some aspect of birth or parenthood: for example, there are organizations for working mothers, too, as well as for mothers who have undergone some specific problem such as an upsetting caesarean birth. Once again, details can be found in Useful Addresses. Don't be put off by any stereotyped images any groups may have acquired; it is at least worth giving it a try and seeing for yourself.

Where to find support

The Useful Addresses section at the back of this book gives an indication of where to find central groups. Ring the numbers given for general information and perhaps local branches or look in your local telephone directory. Your local doctor's surgery, council or library will also be able to give you information about women's centres, playgroups, postnatal support groups and groups for parents or children with illness or disability.

Someone to talk to

Once you have found someone you really trust, you may well go through a period of overt dependency. Some postnatal counsellors have described how very depressed women have needed to call them constantly, perhaps once an hour through the night, in order to hear the same words of hope and reassurance.

The dynamics of accepting help are unpredictable and may take on a life of their own which sweeps you away with it. Try not to worry about this. If you need the help, you need the help. And, if you do feel guilty at taking up so much of someone's time, you can always do the same for someone else once you feel really better. Besides, in accepting help you are making someone else feel needed and valuable in their turn, which can be deeply strengthening for those who are giving out the help.

Getting better

Recovering from depression is often a gradual process, perhaps an uneven one. One day you may start to feel that life is looking up, only to slide into the familiar misery the same evening. Try not to expect too much of yourself while getting better; take it slowly, day by day. It may take longer because you also have to incorporate the changes made by motherhood; it isn't simply a matter of getting back to your old self, important though that is. But the main point, when you're feeling so wretched, is to hang on to the fact that getting better is a real option.

Suzanne was given antidepressants by her doctor and found that the worst was over within a couple of months although during that time she was hospitalized briefly. Lucy's doctor recommended antidepressants and counselling, which helped her talk through her long-suppressed grief over her father's death and other problems. Both Suzanne and Lucy also found a postnatal support group invaluable. Tara's mother and partner helped her through her depression as Tara felt she didn't want professional or group support. Jenny found the difficulties of the first six months just gradually faded away.

This gives an idea of the different ways in which different people get better. It is worth being flexible about the sort of help you are ready to accept. For example, Tara's way of relying on her family may not work for everyone, although very often your nearest and dearest can be a great source of strength. But you might feel you don't want to overburden your family, to leave them drained or resentful. Indeed, some partners or parents of the depressed woman do insist on her seeking other help when they feel they have come to the end of their own strength, and this can be a healthy move in forcing the woman to get better.

Again, whatever help you have, it is important to make sure that it doesn't just skim the surface, that any underlying problems are tackled also, as in Lucy's case. This secondary sorting out of problems can continue for a while even after you've recovered your main emotional balance.

Marcia's doctor was generous with support but didn't feel medication was appropriate; she also had the problem of her weight. Eventually a friend agreed to pick her up to take her to her support group in the evening while her husband stayed with the baby. Discussion inevitably focused on self-image and reasons for over-eating which Marcia found disturbing in a group context. She decided to go to a therapist privately for a few sessions before rejoining the group; this whole process took about two years.

In this case, depression served a long-term useful purpose in forcing Marcia to improve her life. (The whole question of depression's 'message' is discussed further in the Coda.) First, concentrate on getting over the brunt of the depression before intellectualizing the event. Don't pander to any guilt you may have during this process, and don't feel obliged to fall in with people who make you feel humiliated or that you're a 'bad mother': self-help does not mean self-punishment. Be as good to yourself as possible and look for help which makes *you* feel better.

10

You and Your Baby

One of the saddest aspects of postnatal depression is the way it can overshadow the relationship with the baby. Some women feel guilty and disappointed that they don't experience the expected gush of love towards their baby, or fear they've been negligent in caring for her, or sometimes even feel she'd be better off without her mother. Others treasure their baby but fear desperately for his safety, health or happiness, or have a morbid terror of having brought life into an unpredictable world. Others are frightened or irritated by the baby's constant demands, or are stuck with a problem which seems to become bigger and bigger, like a crying baby, or one who won't feed.

None of this need stop you being a good mother. Indeed, some such emotions are quite normal in the mother and baby relationship even if you aren't depressed. Our fear of the more ambivalent feelings stem partly from the social pressure discussed earlier that mothers and babies be all-in-all to each other, and that mothers be perfect madonnas. Ignorance about babies is another factor: babies as well as mothers are imperfect human beings, who cry, refuse feeds and won't sleep even with the most untiring love. Every mother finds her ideas of motherhood upset to some extent by the reality of the baby; every mother has to do not always what she would like, but simply what she can. In postnatal depression, ambivalent feelings become more threatening, but it is vital to try and hold on to some confidence in yourself as a mother, not to let the depression erode it all. Look for areas of strength: maybe you can't feel passionate about the baby yet but are trying to make up with punctilious physical care; maybe you guiltily gave up breastfeeding, but are making sure the baby does get plenty of food via the bottle; maybe you can't bring yourself to go out and give the baby a stimulating change of scene but are giving him plenty of cuddles (and he probably doesn't need the stimulus anyway). Try thinking of at least two positive aspects about the way you care for your baby and focus on these until you can find more.

It also needs to be stressed that not every woman experiences difficulties with her baby.

Louise was beset with marital and housing problems of all kinds, the stress of which she believed had made her baby arrive a month early. Her foreign husband was being threatened with deportation, while she was housed in one room in a council house. An educated girl, she'd let her career go, and all attempts at 'bettering herself'. It was hardly surprising that she should be depressed, and too confused to do anything than leave her problems in the hands of the local authorities. When asked about the baby, however, she glowed visibly: 'Oh, the baby's the best bit of it! She's wonderful!' For Louise, walks in the park with the baby, careful attention to its nappy and bottles, provided the one secure spot in a life fraught with insecurity.

As this story shows, the baby can be the main source of satisfaction and delight in postnatal depression, the only thing which makes the whole experience bearable. Do allow yourself to enjoy your baby as much as you possibly can.

Will my depression affect the baby?

This is a very common fear. It is true that children even when tiny are sensitive to their parents' moods, but this mustn't be made out to be more than it is. In the early weeks of life for example, babies are much more likely to cry because they're hungry than because you are feeling down.

Suzanne had a constantly crying baby and she felt the problem was caused by tensions between herself and her husband. Worried that this might affect the baby, she plucked up courage to approach her doctor who asked, 'How's the feeding going?' Suzanne was initially furious that her emotional problems had been swept under the carpet in this way, but when she offered the baby complementary bottles, they were accepted so eagerly that she wished she'd taken advice earlier. (See 'Crying babies' below.)

As this story shows, the pressure on women to feel the right feelings towards their babies is sometimes at the expense of more practical babycare. 'Bonding' for example is one of the buzz words associated with motherhood which has done most to perpetrate an unrealistic idea of the demands of the mother–child relationship. It implies a simplification of what is often a complex and lengthy process — the establishing of a relationship with a new baby. You don't have to fulfil your own or anyone else's fantasy of motherhood to take adequate care of your baby; even in depression, you can go a long way with the basics of feeding, changing and just holding the baby.

Far more demanding than depression is being aggressive towards a child, though while depression can make you more short-fused than usual, irritability doesn't *have* to be directed at the baby. Many women, though very depressed, never become angry with their babies, as Lucy describes:

> 'I'd get angry with my mother and my husband, but never with the baby – in fact I think it might have been healthier if I had allowed myself to feel some anger at the way she'd disrupted my life.'

If you feel your feelings are leading you towards active aggression, though, do get help. Don't forget you can do this anonymously if you can't bear to go to the doctor's. Listed at the back of this book are a number of organizations you can call for a talk on the phone which may be enough to puncture your mood (see Useful Addresses). And it can sometimes be useful to remind yourself that you don't have to tell your nearest and dearest about such a call for help if you think they are going to be unduly alarmed, so long as you are coping in your own way, without giving in to feelings of aggression.

Both Lucy's and Suzanne's stories mentioned anger with those around them. It is unrealistic to expect a small child to grow up without ever seeing a family quarrel. Indeed, seeing a quarrel carried through and *resolved* is thought to be a better preparation for life than a uniform blandness which gives no hint of the rigours of the outside world. On the other hand, constant long-term anger does create an atmosphere of tension which is not comfortable to grow up in. If you can get to the source of grievances and talk them over frankly, this can be helpful, but it may be beyond you if you are really depressed and just looking for things to hit out at. In this case, make rational discussion an aim for the future, and for now try not to express irritation in front of the baby; and try and find other outlets for your anger – physical ones help, like punching a pillow or running down the road. Also look for someone detached from the family to talk to. Most of all, what about the effect of your depression on yourself? Putting yourself first for a while, making efforts to get help, will in the long run be better than anything for your baby. The positive aspect is that your depression (especially if you do seek help) is likely to be over well before tension with your partner or others has the chance to disrupt your family life on a permanent basis.

Otherwise, part of postnatal depression is feeling that you are a worse mother than you really are. Try not to listen to those horribly persuasive feelings of guilt and self-loathing. The chances are that you are doing a much better job with the baby than you believe. If you want proof of the resilience of babies, just think of the dozens of newborns who survived being buried in the Mexico City earthquake. Do your best not to worry about the baby: cater for his or her basic needs as best you can, and give yourself some attention.

Letting someone else care for your baby

A few women really cannot cope with the baby, and may have to accept help from a relative, close friend or even a professional for a while. This again doesn't mean they don't love their babies: indeed, a great part of the anguish of this time can be the awareness of the inability to care. Neither does it disqualify them from motherhood for life.

At one point, Suzanne's depression grew so bad that she had to go into hospital for two weeks. After she came out, her baby was cared for by her sister for a few weeks. But, just four months later, Suzanne was back at her job as playgroup leader, the baby tucked up contentedly in the pram. Marcia's baby was cared for by Marcia's mother for seven months – a stressful time all round, but one which didn't deter Marcia from later having a second child with no further problems of depression.

Again, because of our social expectations of mothers, there is a slur attached to not being able to cope with a baby's demands. Yet in a way, handing over the baby to someone else in depression is no different from handing her over in an illness, or even because you are going out to work. Sometimes your own needs have to take priority, for the ultimate good of everyone else. You can't be a good mother if you are too depressed to deal with your baby's needs. Bringing up a child is something which requires all your energy, sanity and good will at the best of times! So, if you do have to let go of your baby for a while, rest assured that it isn't necessarily for ever, and that the baby certainly won't suffer with good substitute care. There's even evidence that in the case of working mothers, early social experience outside the home can be beneficial in making children more confident and outgoing. So do not feel guilty about accepting the help that will eventually enable you to get on with motherhood as you'd like. In fact, it is wise to accept this kind of help sooner rather than later – to choose it before it's forced upon you. Many mothers would like more relief from their babies than they get, and perhaps if such help were institutionalized the desperation point would be reached less often. Imagine if the social worker's job was to come round to every mother once a week and babysit for the day so the mother could go out or relax!

Babycare when depressed

Looking after a baby is a highly tiring job at any time. When you're depressed, you often have to overcome quite formidable mental barriers to perform even the simplest of jobs, such as changing a nappy, as Sandra describes:

'You know the baby needs a change, you feel uncomfortable about leaving her, yet you somehow can't bring yourself to plonk her down on that changing mat. It all seems like too much trouble; you genuinely feel too tired to do it; and besides, she'll only dirty the nappy again.'

Then of course the feelings of guilt start escalating, so that what was once a simple job ends up loaded with moral overtones. Work out the worst aspect of babycare for you: the broken nights? breastfeeding? the never-ending routine chores? a crying baby? Some women do find there is a central problem on which the depression seems to focus. For others, it's the general shock of a baby, who may well be far more wakeful and demanding than you expected. Rest assured that an alert, sociable baby is quite normal – babies just don't sleep all the time! Meanwhile, don't worry about doing it all perfectly: concentrate on being adequate, on getting by, on making it as easy as possible on *yourself*, even if it means letting some expectations go.

Crying baby

A baby who cries constantly and won't be comforted is one of the most distressing aspects of motherhood. If you're suffering from postnatal depression, you may well be more sensitive to noise than normal and find the crying more grating; you may also perceive the crying to last longer than it actually does. Research has shown that it is quite normal for a newborn to cry for a total of around two hours a day. This is not to minimize your distress, or even to say that you should find this level of crying acceptable; but you certainly should not blame yourself or your depression for the crying. As Suzanne's story above shows, sheer hunger is often an underestimated cause for crying and is always worth checking first. Illness should also be borne in mind: look out for a raised temperature, vomiting, diarrhoea, floppiness, glazed eyes, or if your baby puts a hand up to his head or ear. Do consult your doctor about constant crying, to rule out the possibility of a physical cause.

Other causes are wanting to be held, cold, nappy discomfort or rash, overstimulation, tiredness, and so-called colic; there are also many theories about babies crying out the pain they experienced during childbirth, and other factors over all of which you are equally powerless.

Try and sort out what you can do, and what you can't. After checking for a physical cause, other methods of soothing are cuddling, rocking, swaddling, playing rhythmic music, walking out in a pushchair or taking for a car ride. If your baby has colic (crying in the evening with legs drawn up beneath her) she will be hard, often impossible to pacify, though you can try rubbing her tummy, or giving her a warm bath. Colic does usually pass off around the end of the third month (consult your doctor if it doesn't).

It is this sort of crying which can push you over the edge into depression; for example, if you're still tired after the birth and obliged to pace the floors endlessly at night. A crying baby is very draining, so look after yourself if you can't stop the crying and if your doctor has given your baby the all-clear. Get your partner or other friends to take turns with holding the baby, and get what rest you can at other times – the crying will pass eventually. If you're alone and you get desperate, put the baby down in her cot and leave her for five minutes; go to a part of the house where she's less audible; have a snack or milky drink, practise stretching or deep breathing; call someone for help; or take the baby out in her sling or pushchair. (See Useful Addresses for a support group.)

Coping with a night-waker

If mothers were sent home from the postnatal ward with sleep-training charts as well as exercise leaflets, life with a new baby might be radically different! It would help at least if mothers had a realistic idea of how often a tiny baby wakes up at night, and at what age he should be expected to sleep through. All new babies wake at night, and the baby who is sleeping through the night by three months is the exception rather than the rule. It is also probably true that many babies are allowed to go on waking up at night beyond an age when they might reasonably be expected to sleep through.

Many mothers might raise an eyebrow at the way 'changes in sleeping patterns' is blandly trotted forth as a symptom of postnatal depression, especially when they read the proviso, 'It can be hard to spot changes in sleeping patterns because the baby disturbs these anyway.' As Jenny comments:

'It's hardly surprising really that women get depressed because the baby can disturb your sleep so much. It's the constant getting up at night, the Chinese water torture of the baby waking you up for the fifth time just as you've dropped off, the utter dreariness of having to get up at 5 a.m. after a really broken night because the baby's up for the day then.'

Other mothers, however, believe that the loss of sleep *per se* isn't enough to cause the gripping depression they suffered from.

When Tara's little boy became ill, a year after she'd recovered from her depression, she was struck by the fact that, contrary to her fears, three weeks of broken nights didn't bring back her depression, although of course by then she didn't have to cope with the aftermath of a draining pregnancy and stressful delivery.

All in all, it can sometimes be hard to decide which came first, the disturbed sleep or the depression. The inability to go back to sleep once woken has often been cited as a symptom of postnatal depression, but with a frequent waker it can be very hard to sink back into slumber after the third time of being woken. This is especially so if you feel obliged to get up every time the baby cried at night, sit correctly in the armless breastfeeding chair, arrange a couple of pillows, feed for twenty minutes, and then try and go back to sleep, burning with resentment because you're now thoroughly awake!

One of the easiest ways of coping with a night-waker is just to take him into bed with you. It has been shown that, unless parents drink heavily or drug, they instinctively keep clear of the baby during sleep, and it is most unlikely that they would roll onto him. Sleeping together can also help the relationship between you and your baby, giving you more comfort and confidence if you are depressed. Giving up trying to win with your baby, trying to *make* him sleep, can also relieve a lot of tension: if he is happier sleeping with you, and you can get more sleep this way too, why not just accept it?

Another idea is to ask your doctor or health visitor to work on a sleep-training plan with you when the baby is a little older. There's little point trying to 'train' a baby under the age of six months to sleep at certain times, because she can't understand; training is more effective and tends to last longer if done after the baby is a year old. Getting a baby to sleep through does demand commitment, so do get help and advice. (See Further Reading for more information.) You can also consider compromises: sleeping in a bed next to your child's cot or installing her in a 'half-bed' or cot with the side down next to your bed. None of these compromises are perfect, but they may be enough to get you past a difficult sleeping period, when you're depressed and need more sleep, but can't get it because of a waking baby.

If *you* can't sleep, try not to worry, and rest as much as you can instead. And do ask your doctor for help in breaking a pattern which has become disturbing and destructive. To repeat what has been said above, don't suffer sleeplessness or broken nights alone. If your doctor can't help, try a second opinion or contact a support group for advice (see Useful Addresses, and 'Coping with tiredness' in chapter 9).

Breastfeeding

Something which the advocates of breastfeeding seem occasionally reluctant to allow is how draining breastfeeding can be. Given the exhaustion that many depressed mothers feel, this is a serious consideration. But giving up breastfeeding can be daunting to a depressed mother's already battered confidence. Breast milk does provide babies with a good start in life, but it is a shame that this recognition has become yet another pressure for mothers.

At eight weeks, Suzanne's baby still looked like a newborn – or was at least appreciably smaller in size than babies of two friends born at the same time. The baby cried constantly, with Suzanne coming a close second! She compared herself constantly with her breastfeeding friends and was at her wits' end until the doctor ordered her to switch to bottle feeding. Within days the baby started putting on weight and became much more content.

The peer or social pressure to breastfeed can be very strong ('breast is best') and the more you try to breastfeed and 'fail' the worse you feel. For some women, breastfeeding then turns into a battle in which the burden of proof is on them, and they can put themselves through great emotional and physical distress before finally giving up.

Antonia's baby wanted to feed all the time, and she was convinced she didn't have enough milk. Her breasts were always sore from the baby's continual suckling, she felt weak and used up, and hated the let-down reflex, which was not only painful but caused a great feeling of depression and bleakness to go through her. Finally her mother persuaded her to try the baby on a bottle; the baby took to it well, and Antonia felt much better for the change.

It can be seen here that a tussle was involved between Antonia and her mother: the natural urge to surpass the last generation, to prove that you can be a mother in your own way, not in your own mother's way. In short, breastfeeding can be a focus for all sorts of emotional conflict and is an area where a depressed mother may feel particularly sensitive to her image as reflected by her ability to cope.

If you want to continue breastfeeding but are having difficulties, one way to increase your milk flow is simply to put your feet up for two or three days, eat and drink plentifully, and suckle the baby on demand. Otherwise, it might be helpful to contact a breastfeeding support group. But don't feel obliged to follow any suggestions made or to continue with breastfeeding if it is causing you pain or distress.

Some women have stated how their depression 'really took off' when they stopped breastfeeding. This is thought to be allied to hormonal changes which take place at this time and which bring about the return of menstruation (see chapter 8 for more on hormones, postnatal depression, and pre-menstrual tension). However, you have to stop breastfeeding some time and forewarned is forearmed. Keep a diary of your reactions as you stop feeding, and on into your periods, so that you are more aware of pre-menstrual tension if it does begin.

Other children

If you have postnatal depression with a second, third or fourth baby, you are likely to be distressed about the effect it may have on your other children. What can you do? First, explain to them, as far as their age and understanding allows, that you are not feeling well, but that you will be better later, and tell them that it isn't their fault – children do tend to believe that they are the centre and cause of everything.

Do accept the help of family and friends, both to look after the children themselves and to look after the baby so you can give older children some undivided time and attention. Pin-point your most difficult time of day and see if you can arrange for extra help then: for example, someone to take an older child to school in the morning when you are hurried and stressed. If your older child is coming up for playgroup age (two and a half), see if it's possible to get him started a bit earlier. Some playgroups will allow an earlier start if you stay with the child, which is company for you and a way of getting out of the house, as well as giving your child more to do.

Routine and the reality

We all need routine in our lives but the word seems to have acquired distinctly menacing overtones in connection with babies. Routine builds up until it acquires a life of its own, almost becoming an extra member of the family, and a rather forbidding, limiting one at that. You may have heard other mothers or yourself come out with self-imposed necessities: 'I'll try and join you for coffee but James usually has a sleep then'; 'We'll come to tea but we have to be back by six because I have to start putting him to bed then'; 'I'm dreading going on holiday because I know it will ruin his routine.'

Sticking to a 'routine' may be difficult or impossible in depression. It can be helpful to forget all about routine and instead try and work out which is the worst part of the day for you. Instead of set events at set times, think about seeing the day in terms of basic needs, such as eating, dressing, washing and resting. Also try and include the following in your day, one or all of them: one outing a day even if it's just a walk to the post box; one cooked snack or meal, such as scrambled eggs or vegetable soup if you can't manage more; one phone call to a friend; one piece of physical attention such as a bath, manicure, facial scrub, massaging your stretch marks, and so on.

Starting and ending the day

A broken night followed by an early morning start is a fairly classic start for many depressed mothers of young babies.

Jenny would be woken by the baby at 5.30 a.m. sharp every day and feel obliged to get up and take the child downstairs so that her partner could sleep before going out to work. Invariably she would end up feeling 'shaky and drained' by 9 a.m. – the time she used to start work. She would try to boost herself with coffee and biscuits, but all too often ended up losing her temper over something trivial and then subsiding into exhaustion.

Starting the day can help influence the rest of its course; if you do find first thing in the morning difficult, make an effort to relax. Don't get up at once, driven by feelings of doom: stay in bed and make an effort to eat and drink something – the usual cup of tea and biscuits – at least for a few minutes, longer if you can. Have a wakeful baby in with you for a cuddle and/or feed. It is a problem when a partner has to go to work and wants to sleep on; some couples have solved it for a while by sleeping separately; another idea is to take it in turns to get up with the baby. If you're the one who's getting up, make yourself as warm and comfortable as possible in another room – you still don't have to start the day yet. If you can, reach for something to read soon after waking, so that your mind doesn't have a chance to fall back into its usual depressed chatter, even if you only manage a page or two.

Jenny stopped feeling obliged to get up at 5.30 a.m.: even if she woke up then, she would bring the baby into her bed for a cuddle and sometimes fall asleep again, give him a bottle in bed, or lie dozing herself while he played with his toys and ate a rusk. Her partner, who normally slept until around 7 a.m., would get up at 6 a.m. to bring them both tea and biscuits in bed.

115

You may find that, like many mothers with postnatal depression, you have more energy for a few hours in the mornings, followed by a dip in the long, wearisome afternoons. For this reason afternoon can be a good time to try and get out or see people. Later, with a partner arriving home from work and everyone tired from the day, evening is a time when the deadly hand of routine can be more than usually punishing.

Lucy would frequently wonder how she could muster the strength to go through it all *again* – the bath, the book, the story, the last feed, the nappy change, the change into pyjamas, the last cuddle, not to mention the scene when she tried to leave the bedroom. The whole 'bedtime routine' was taking about two hours every night, leaving her even more exhausted.

Part of the problem is that it is often difficult to see a way of changing things when you're stuck in them, above all when depressed. However, there are ways in which you can make life easier for yourself, if you are willing to change your ideas. Once you've pin-pointed your 'difficult time' you can see if there is anything which can be done, even if it entails letting your standards drop.

Lucy's husband somewhat exasperatedly pointed out that she didn't have to go through it all every night, that there were other ways of putting a child to bed. For several days after, Lucy would change the baby into pyjamas and just let him fall asleep on a bottle as she and her husband watched television together. 'Had anyone told me I'd be doing that when the baby was born, I would have been horrified', said Lucy. 'But that time relaxing alone together did help save my sanity – perhaps my marriage, too.'

Increased flexibility is often forced upon you by the baby, so, forget the high aspirations: just look round for the easiest way to do things right now. This phase will not last for ever.

Lower your expectations

On this note, some women have spoken of how their depression was made worse by their high expectations of motherhood and of life in general.

When Lucy, herself a victim of high expectations, had recovered from her depression, she was amused by a pregnant friend of hers whose hobby was mountaineering. The friend excitedly announced how she and her partner were going to take the new baby camping up a mountain in the autumn. Lucy pointed out it might be too cold for the baby, while Lucy's husband said, 'Frankly, you'll be doing well if you can get out through the door in the first year!'

It pays to be realistic about how far you can expect the baby to slot into a previous lifestyle, and to try and understand how your expectations of life with a baby may have paved the way for postnatal depression. The gap between what you visualized, and what actually happens as you struggle with the nitty-gritty of babycare, can leave room for a certain grieving. It can be hard to let go of the image you may have had of yourself as a mother: but, to repeat what was said earlier in this chapter, make an effort to focus on your strengths, your warmth and the love you have for your baby, even when you may be saddened at not always being able to feel that love as you think a mother 'should'.

Coda
Listen to Postnatal Depression

Does postnatal depression in fact have anything to say? Anything worth hearing, anything which will make a positive difference to your life? Or is it a purely negative experience, to be got through and forgotten as fast as possible?

On one level, the 'message' of postnatal depression has been interpreted as a social one, crying out that things aren't good enough for mothers, with a slow-to-support and quick-to-blame social ethos which increases parents' isolation. Some might argue that the whole question of the experience having value is out of place, that adequate hormonal, anti-depressant, counselling or other treatment is of far more value, and that describing illness as 'character-building' or 'spiritually educational' is woefully beside the point. Others might feel that the experience has value as a pointer to underlying depressive tendencies or previously existing mental problems which can then be treated. The really important question however is whether postnatal depression has had meaning for you.

Some people do shrug it off as 'just one of those things', and aim to forget it and get on with life. Others remain intrigued by their experience but puzzled, not quite sure what to make of it, perhaps keen to know more about postnatal depression before coming to any conclusions; a few become crusaders for the postnatal depression cause, helping spread information and doing volunteer work with other sufferers. Others can be much more definite and point to certain things which they learned from the experience. Perhaps you have experienced something of all these reactions.

Lucy did feel that her experience had been a teacher.
'I feel I won't ever be as happy again as I was before, but that doesn't really matter because in a way it was a fairly unthinking happiness. I was the sort who never had any mental or emotional troubles, and now I feel a whole other side of life has opened up to me. If it wasn't for the depression, I'd never have started thinking in terms of personal growth, discovery.'
Lucy's sense of her gains from depression was subtle and far-ranging, so that to call it 'growth' sounds rather too blunt and undeveloped. In place of her previous 'unthinking happiness' which took life for granted and denied pain and wasted time, she came to a more vulnerable stance which yet had room for release and excitement.

118

'I think it's a more balanced view of life – I used to just charge around before, like a schoolgirl. Now I feel much stronger for what happened. I've learnt a lot. You don't know what life has round the corner – life and happiness are precarious, but I feel strong enough to deal with it, good and bad.'

Looking at it as a growing experience is perhaps the easier because postnatal depression comes at a time when having a baby naturally invites you to become more adult. Indeed, it could be said that postnatal depression offers the chance to become infantile just at the time when childhood should be put away, and such a deep conflict between immature and mature needs will inevitably lead to self-discovery and growth. Depression can pull all your defences down, leaving you more open to long-term external change as well as internal. For some people, it has marked a fairly definite turning-point in their lives. Antonia, who had once travelled widely as a photographer, gave up her career:

'I took up painting and pottery – rather shamefacedly. I felt I was being terribly self-indulgent and middle class. But I felt that my career had peaked and I wasn't going to get any more out of it, and I wanted to spend time at home with the baby. It was quite a big decision, and at first I felt I was just mucking about. But then I started to sell stuff and I realized that I could make a modest living as an artist – the emphasis on modest! If nothing else, it helped those awful black moods when I just wanted to lie down and cry or get under the bed and hide – doing something with my fingers, that needed attention. I would have done it anyway as creative therapy. It was certainly better than medication for me – I didn't take antidepressants.'

Antonia's self-deprecatory remarks show how the low self-worth behind depression can cancel out new projects before you've even tried – 'self-indulgent' and 'only mucking about'. Depression can, however, be a motivator in urging you to seek some creative outlet in your life, and many mothers do change career course after having a baby. On a more pragmatic note, however, just as pain is the body's protest against illness or injury, could depression be a protest about certain aspects of your life right now? In this book, emphasis has been laid on the mother's need to rest, and depression, with its urge to do nothing, can perhaps be used to achieve this objective.

Marcia, who had such trouble sleeping, spent most of her days worrying about the effect lack of sleep was having on her. Her main complaint was that she didn't feel like doing anything. One of the things which helped her was her mother-in-law telling her, 'Don't do anything, then! Sometimes we need to do nothing.'

Implicit in Marcia's remarks above is a feeling that, in order to be a worthy person, she should be making good use of her time. Lucy refers to something similar in her remarks above ('wasted time'). We are used to being seen to be working, to being productive, something which can undercut the very real need for extra rest after a birth. Depression can certainly bring another dimension to time, as Lucy explains:

'You realize that time isn't necessarily yours to do what you want with, to achieve things in, as you may have thought before. With work, I'd had such pressure to achieve, to get things done, to say so much and teach so much within a given period. That structure falls apart completely with a baby – your time isn't being monitored or paid for, no one cares how you spend it, so if your self-worth is low, how do you know if your time is valid or not? You have to be so much more self-reliant, to look for other values. I realized there was something very mechanical about the way I'd been so busy before, flying from person to person, filling in time.'

A greater sense of contentment in her own company was one of the benefits Lucy felt she had gained from her experience of depression, an increased sense of self which no longer needed so much bolstering from the company of others. So, listen to any weariness and take the rest you need; do slow down if you feel you need to. This isn't to condemn all activity: if you thrive on being busy, it could be a question of seeking different outlets for your energy. Is your depression a weariness with certain aspects of your life which you feel you're outgrowing as you go through the changes brought by motherhood?

The isolation created by postnatal depression has another dimension in that you aren't really alone: you have the baby. The negative side of this solitude has been stressed, but it can be of value in nestling down and spending irreplaceable time with your child.

Tara went on holiday to the country and was impressed by seeing a horse with a new foal who refused to be coaxed to the fence.

'She would prick up her ears and see the bit of apple I was holding, then she'd whinny and trot off and then look at me again, hovering round her foal all the time. The two of them were so isolated in this big, wild marshland. It suddenly struck me – she wasn't worried about coming near me, why should I worry about being with people myself? Maybe that my own feelings of isolation could be serving a useful point – maybe they were even biological – in protecting the baby and making sure we stayed together. Maybe that was part of why I hated leaving the house so much when I was depressed.'

This positive aspect of isolation – time alone with the baby – can sometimes be overlooked, although when you are very depressed, of course, it can be just as important – if not more so – to have company. Once the depression has passed, some women have said that one of the positive long-term results is the feeling of fellowship they now have with others who are going through a similar impoverishment, a similar 'black hole'. As Suzanne put it:

'I feel I've joined a secret society – I've been on the other side, and I can recognize the other people who are there now, in that unhappiness. Now, when anyone's unhappy, my antennae pick it up. In a room full of mothers, I can practically pick out the ones who are suffering from postnatal depression. As a playgroup leader it's certainly added something to my life – my job is to look after the children but I now also feel I have a duty towards the mums.'

For some women, then, postnatal depression can be taken as a message pointing to special areas of their lives or themselves that can be changed: their thinking, the way they see themselves and others, the way they spend their time. It is certainly worth making time to sit down quietly and just think about what the depression may be trying to 'tell' you. It can range from deep, psychological conflicts, unresolved from your earliest years, to the appalled realization that babycare is difficult and time-demanding. Whatever you find, however you interpret your experience, postnatal depression is not the end of the road; or, if it is the end of one road, it can be the beginning of another.

Further Reading

Balaskas, J. *New Active Birth*, Thorsons 1991.

Barnes, Tricia and Rodwell, Lee *A Woman's Guide to Loving Sex*, Boxtree 1992.

Clement, Sarah *The Caesarean Experience*, Pandora 1992.

Comport, Maggie *Towards Happy Motherhood: Understanding Postnatal Depression*, Corgi 1987.

Dalton, Dr Katherine *Depression after Childbirth*, Oxford University Press 1992.

Dix, Carol *The New Mother Syndrome*, Unwin 1985.

Douglas, Jo and Richman, Naomi *My Child Won't Sleep*, Penguin Books 1990.

Eason, Cassandra *A Mother's Instincts*, Aquarian Press 1993.

Gray, Pat *Crying Baby: How to Cope*, Wisebuy Publications, 1987. Available from bookshops or from Cry-sis, 121 Melbourne Road, Garden Village, Stocksbridge, Sheffield S30 5EF, £3.50 plus 50p post and packing.

Health Education Authority, *Breastfeeding: Your Questions Answered*. Available free from the Distribution Section, Health Education Authority, Hamilton House, Mabledon Place, London WC1H 9TX.

Murphy, Sarah *Talking about Miscarriage*, Sheldon Press 1992.

Planer, Nigel *A Good Enough Dad: The True Confessions of an Infant Father*, Ebury Press 1992.

Polden, Margie and Whiteford, Barbara *The Postnatal Exercise Book*, Frances Lincoln 1992.

Priya, Vincent Jacqueline *Birth Traditions and Modern Pregnancy Care*, Element Books 1992.

Roeber, Johanna *Shared Parenthood: A Handbook for Fathers*, Century Hutchinson 1987.

Sapstead, Anne Marie *Banish Post-Baby Blues*, Thorsons 1990.

Useful Addresses

These are the national or London branches – you can also look in your phone book for local branches. If writing, an SAE is usually appreciated.

Alcoholics Anonymous, General Service Office, PO Box 1, Stonebow House, York YO1 2N5. Tel: 0904 644026 (or local directory).

The Association for Post-Natal Illness (APNI), 25 Jerdan Place, London SW6 1BE. Tel: 071–386 0868. (10 a.m.–2 p.m. Monday to Friday. Information and help on postnatal depression.)

Association of Breastfeeding Mothers, 26 Holmshaw Close, London SE26 4TH. Tel: 081–778 4769.

Bliss (Baby Life Support Systems), 17–21 Emerald Street, London WC1N 3QL. Blisslink: 071–831 9393. (Support for parents of special care babies.)

Caesarean Support Group (NCT), call National Childbirth Trust for details.

Caesarean Support Network, c/o 55 Cooil Drive, Douglas, Isle of Man. Tel: 0624 620647.

Contact a Family, 16 Strutton Ground, London SW1P 2HP. Tel: 071–222 2695 (For families of children with special needs.)

Cry-sis, BM Cry-sis, London WC1N 3XX. Tel: 071–404 5011. (For parents suffering from a crying baby.)

Episiotomy Support, Avon Episiotomy Support Group, PO Box 130, Weston-Super-Mare, Avon BS23 4YJ.

Gingerbread Association for One Parent Families, 35 Wellington Street, London WC2E 7BN. Tel: 071–240 0953.

The Institute for Complementary Medicine, PO Box 194, London SE16 1QZ. Tel: 071–237 5165.

La Leche League, BM 3424, London WC1N 3XX. Tel: 071–242 1278. (Information and support on breastfeeding.)

Meet-a-Mum Association (MAMA), 58 Malden Avenue, South Norwood, London SE25 4HS. Tel: 081–656 7318. (Contact with mothers and help with postnatal depression.)

MIND (National Association for Mental Health), 22 Harley Street, London W1N 2ED. Tel: 071–637 0741. (Help with mental illness.)

The Miscarriage Association, PO Box 24, Ossett, West Yorkshire WF5 9XG. Tel: 0924 830515.

The National Childbirth Trust, Alexandra House, Oldham Terrace, London W3 6NH. Tel: 081–992 8637.

The National Debtline, Tel: 021–359 8501. (For anyone in debt.)

Nippers, Tel: 0934 733123. (For parents of pre-term and special care babies.)

Parentline National Office, Westbury House, 57 Hart Road, Thundersley, Essex SS7 3PD. Tel: 0268 757077.

Parent Network, 44–46 Caversham Road, London NW5 2DS. Tel: 071–485 8535.

Overeaters Anonymous Great Britain, PO Box 19, Stretford, Manchester M32 1EB. Tel: 071–498 5505.

Parents Anonymous, 8 Manor Gardens, London N7 6LA. Tel: 071–263 8918.

Quitline, Tel: 071–487 3000. (For those who want to stop smoking.)

RELATE: Marriage Guidance Council, Head Office, Herbert Gray College, Little Church Street, Rugby, Warwickshire CV21 3AP. Tel: 0788 573241.

The Samaritans, 46 Marshall Street, London W1V 1LR. Tel: 071–734 2800.

Society to Support Home Confinement, Lydgate House, Lydgate Lane, Wolsingham, Durham DL13 3HA. Tel: 0388 528044 (after 6 p.m.).

Index

INDEX

sleeping problems 2, 12
social factors 58–69
suicide 9, 77
support groups 102–3

tension 13
termination, of pregnancy 26

thyroid deficiency 91
twin birth 54

varicose veins 92

weight *see* body image
working mothers 62–4